PEARSON   ALWAYS LEARNING

Scott Freeman • Jean Heitz • Cynthia Giffen

Practicing Biology

A Student Workbook
for Biological Science

A Second Custom Edition for Emory University

Taken from:
Practicing Biology: A Student Workbook for Biological Science,
Fourth Edition
by Scott Freeman compiled by Jean Heitz and Cynthia Giffen

Cover Art: Courtesy of Photodisc/Getty Images.

Taken from:

Practicing Biology: A Student Workbook for Biological Science, Fourth Edition,
by Scott Freeman compiled by Jean Heitz and Cynthia Giffen
Copyright © 2011, 2008, 2005 by Pearson Education, Inc.
Published by Benjamin Cummings
San Francisco, California 94111

Pearson Learning Solutions, 501 Boylston Street, Suite 900, Boston, MA 02116
A Pearson Education Company
www.pearsoned.com

Printed in the United States of America

1 2 3 4 5 6 7 8 9 10 V313 16 15 14 13 12 11

000200010270759168

JL

ISBN 10: 1-256-13982-3
ISBN 13: 978-1-256-13982-9

Contents

Contents

Contents

Contents

Name ——————————————— Course/Section ———————————————

Date ——————————————— Professor/TA ———————————————

  Activity 2.1 A Quick Review of Elements and Compounds

1. Figure 2.3 (page 17 of *Biological Science*, 4th ed.) lists the chemical elements that occur naturally in the human body. Similar percentages of these elements are found in most living organisms.

a. In what abiotic (nonlife) chemical forms are these elements often found in nature?	b. In what chemical form(s) do animals need to obtain these elements?	c. In what chemical form(s) do plants need to obtain these elements?

2. A chemical element cannot be broken down to other forms by chemical reactions. Each element has a specific number of protons, neutrons, and electrons.

   a. What is the name of the following element, and how many protons, neutrons, and electrons does it have?

$$
\boxed{\begin{array}{c} 11 \\ \textsf{Na} \\ 23 \end{array}}
$$

Name	Number of protons	Number of neutrons	Number of electrons

b. What information do you need to calculate or to determine the following?

The atomic number of an element	The mass number of an element	The weight in atomic mass units (daltons) of one atom of an element

c. What are the atomic number, mass number, and weight in atomic mass units (daltons) of the element shown in part a?

Atomic number	Mass number	Weight in atomic mass units

3. One mole of an element or compound contains 6.02×10^{23} atoms or molecules of the element or compound. One mole of an element or compound has a mass equal to its mass number (or molecular weight) in grams. For example, 1 mole of hydrogen gas (H_2) contains 6.02×10^{23} molecules and weighs 2 g.

a. What is the weight of 1 mole of pure sodium (Na)?	b. How many molecules of Na are in 1 mole of Na?

c. How would you determine how many grams are in a mole of any chemical element or compound?

4. One atom of Na can combine with one atom of Cl (chlorine) to produce one molecule of NaCl (table salt).

a. If Cl has 17 electrons, 17 protons, and 18 neutrons, what is its mass number?	b. What is the mass number of NaCl?	c. How many grams of NaCl equal a mole of NaCl?

d. If you wanted to combine equal numbers of Na and Cl atoms in a flask, how much Cl would you have to add if you added 23 g of Na? (Explain the reasoning behind your answer.)

e. To make a one-molar (1 *M*) solution of NaCl, you need to add 1 mole of NaCl to distilled water to make a final volume of 1 L (1000 ml). A 1 *M* solution is said to have a molarity of 1. If you added 2 moles of NaCl to distilled water to make a final volume of 1 L, you would make a 2 *M* solution and its molarity would equal 2.

You make up a 1 *M* solution of NaCl.

How many molecules of NaCl are in the 1 *M* NaCl solution?	How many molecules of NaCl are there per ml of the solution?

f. Next, you divide this 1 *M* solution of NaCl into four separate flasks, putting 250 ml into each flask.

How many grams of NaCl are in each flask?	How many molecules of NaCl are in each flask?	How many molecules of NaCl are there per ml of distilled water?	What is the molarity of NaCl in each of the four flasks?

5. The summary formula for photosynthesis is

$$6 \, CO_2 + 6 \, H_2O \longrightarrow C_6H_{12}O_6 + 6 \, O_2$$

a. How many molecules of carbon dioxide and water would a plant have to use to produce 3 molecules of glucose ($C_6H_{12}O_6$)?	b. How many moles of carbon dioxide and water would a plant have to use to produce 2 moles of glucose?

c. Refer to the summary formula for photosynthesis. If you know the number of molecules or moles of any of the reactants used (or products produced), how would you calculate the number of molecules or moles of all of the other reactants needed and products produced?

6. A biologist places a plant in a closed chamber. A sensor in the chamber maintains the carbon dioxide level at the normal atmospheric concentration of 0.03%. Another sensor allows the biologist to measure the amount of oxygen produced by the plant over time. If the plant produces 0.001 mole of oxygen in an hour, how much carbon dioxide had to be added to the chamber during that hour to maintain the atmospheric concentration of 0.03%?

7. Refer to pages 20–27 of your textbook for a description of types of chemical bonds: nonpolar and polar covalent bonds, ionic bonds, and hydrogen bonds. (The molecule diagrammed here can also be represented by the formula CH_3COOH.)

Explain how you could determine which of the bonds between elements in this molecule are polar or nonpolar covalent bonds, ionic bonds, and hydrogen bonds.

8. O_2 and NH_3 are both small covalent molecules found in cells. NH_3 is extremely soluble in the aqueous environment of the cell, while O_2 is relatively insoluble. What is the basis for this difference in solubility between the two molecules? In reaching your answer, draw the structures of the molecules as valence shell diagrams (as in Figure 2.8, page 23). Given these diagrams, consider the types of interactions each molecule could have with water.

Name ——————————————   Course/Section ——————————————

Date ——————————————   Professor/TA ——————————————

  Activity 2.2 A Quick Review of the Properties of Water

1. Compounds that have the capacity to form hydrogen bonds with water are said to be
    hydrophilic (water loving). Those without this capacity are hydrophobic (water
    fearing).

H | H—C—C\=O | \OH H	Is the molecule on the left hydrophilic or hydrophobic? Explain your answer.

2. In addition to being polar, water molecules can dissociate into hydronium ions
    (H_3O^+, often described simply as H^+) and hydroxide ions (OH^-). The concentration
    of each of these ions in pure water is 10^{-7}. Another way to say this is that the
    concentration of hydronium ions, or H^+ ions, is one out of every 10 million
    molecules. Similarly, the concentration of OH^- ions is one in 10 million molecules.

    a. The H^+ ion concentration of a solution can be represented as its pH value. The
        pH of a solution is defined as the negative $\log_{10}$ of the hydrogen ion
        concentration. What is the pH of pure water?

    b. Refer to the diagram of the molecule of acetic acid in question 1. The –COOH
        group can ionize to release a H^+ ion into solution. If you add acetic acid to water
        and raise the concentration of H^+ ions to 10^{-4}, what is the pH of this solution?

3. Life as we know it could not exist without water. All the chemical reactions of life occur in aqueous solution. Water molecules are polar and are capable of forming hydrogen bonds with other polar or charged molecules. As a result, water has the following properties:

   A. H_2O molecules are cohesive; they form hydrogen bonds with each other.
   B. H_2O molecules are adhesive; they form hydrogen bonds with polar surfaces.
   C. Water is a liquid at normal physiological (or body) temperatures.
   D. Water has a high specific heat.
   E. Water has a high heat of vaporization.
   F. Water's greatest density occurs at 4°C.

Explain how these properties of water are related to the phenomena described in parts a–h below. More than one property may be used to explain a given phenomenon.

   a. During the winter, air temperatures in the northern United States can remain below 0°C for months; however, the fish and other animals living in the lakes survive.

   b. Many substances—for example, salt (NaCl) and sucrose—dissolve quickly in water.

   c. When you pour water into a 25-ml graduated cylinder, a meniscus forms at the top of the water column.

   d. Sweating and the evaporation of sweat from the body surface help reduce a human's body temperature.

e. A bottle contains a liquid mixture of equal parts water and mineral oil. You shake the bottle vigorously and then set it on the table. Although the law of entropy favors maximum randomness, this mixture separates into layers of oil over water.

f. Water drops that fall on a surface tend to form rounded drops or beads.

g. Water drops that fall on your car tend to bead or round up more after you polish (or wax) the car than before you polished it.

h. If you touch the edge of a paper towel to a drop of colored water, the water will move up into (or be absorbed by) the towel.

Name ——————————————— Course/Section ———————————————

Date ——————————————— Professor/TA ———————————————

Extend Your
Understanding **Activity 2.3 Are silicon-based life forms possible?**

Silicon is very similar to carbon in its chemical properties. For example, both are in the same group of the periodic table, and both Si and C have 4 electrons in their outer shells. Based on these similarities, some science fiction writers have suggested that life-forms on other planets could be silicon-based. Given what you know about the two elements, their reactivity or electronegativity, and the types of compounds they form, indicate whether it is possible that life could be Si-based as well as C-based. Feel free to use additional resources to make an argument for or against a world where silicon forms the building blocks of life.

Name ______________________ Course/Section ______________________

Date ______________________ Professor/TA ______________________

Extend Your Understanding

Activity 2.4 Do chemical reaction rates increase with increased temperature and concentration?

Figure 2.22 on page 31 in the textbook shows data from an experiment designed to determine if chemical reaction rates increase with increased temperature and concentration. Students at Parklawn College tested the effects of temperature and concentration on reaction rate separately, and their results are shown in Figure 2.22. You are a lab technician at a biotech company, and need to determine the fastest way to make large quantities of HSO_4^-. How would you design an experiment to test the combined effects of temperature and concentration on reaction rate in order to optimize the production process? Include the following components in your experimental design: controls, replicates, and concentration and temperatures of reactants. Clearly state your predicted and null hypotheses, and draw a graph of your expected results.

Name _____ Course/Section _____

Date _____ Professor/TA _____

 Activity 3.1 What properties do proteins have?

1. Functional groups can modify the properties of organic molecules. In the table below, indicate whether each functional group is polar or nonpolar and hydrophobic or hydrophilic. Which of these functional groups are found in proteins? Use Table 2.3 on page 35 and Figure 3.3 on page 41 of *Biological Science*, 4th edition, to fill in the table.

Functional group	Polar or nonpolar?	Hydrophobic or hydrophilic?	Found in all proteins?	Found in many proteins?
–OH				
$-CH_2$				
–COOH				
$-NH_2$				
–SH				
$-PO_4$				

2. Twenty amino acids are commonly utilized in the synthesis of proteins. These amino acids differ in the chemical properties of their side chains (also called R-groups). What properties does each of the following R-groups have? (*Note:* A side chain may display more than one of these properties.)

R Group	Basic, acidic, or neutral	Polar or nonpolar	Hydrophilic or hydrophobic
a. CH_2 / CH / CH_3 CH_3			
b. CH_2 / $-O$ $C=O$			
c. CH_2 / CH_2 / CH_2 / CH_2 / NH_3^+			
d. CH_2 / OH			

3. Polypeptides and proteins are made up of linear sequences of amino acids. In its functional form, each protein has a specific three-dimensional structure or shape. Interactions among the individual amino acids and their side chains play a major role in determining this shape.

   a. How are amino acids linked together to form polypeptides or proteins? What is this type of bond called?

b. Define the four structures of a protein.	c. What kinds of bonds hold each of these structures together?
Primary:	
Secondary:	
Tertiary:	
Quaternary:	

d. On the figures below, label at least one of each of the following characteristics of proteins: α-helix, β-pleated sheet, H-bonding along peptide-bonded backbone, and van der Waals interaction.

(a) Cro protein, a dimer

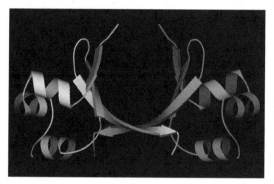

(b) Hemoglobin, a tetramer

e. Describe how the structures above might change if denatured by high heat or by a chemical that can denature protein.

4. Use your understanding of the proteins in living organisms to predict the outcome of the following experiments. Be sure to explain your reasoning.

Experiment a: A globular protein that is ordinarily found in aqueous solution has these amino acids in its primary structure: glutamic acid, lysine, leucine, and tryptophan. Predict where you would find each amino acid: in the interior portion of the protein (away from water) or on the outside of the protein (facing water). (Refer to Figure 3.11 on page 47 of the textbook.)

Experiment b: Drawn below is part of the tertiary structure of a protein showing the positions of two amino acids (aspartic acid and lysine). Replacing lysine with another amino acid in the protein may change the shape and function of the protein. Replacing lysine with which type(s) of amino acid(s) would lead to the least amount of change in the tertiary structure of this protein? (Refer to Figure 3.12a on page 48 of the textbook.)

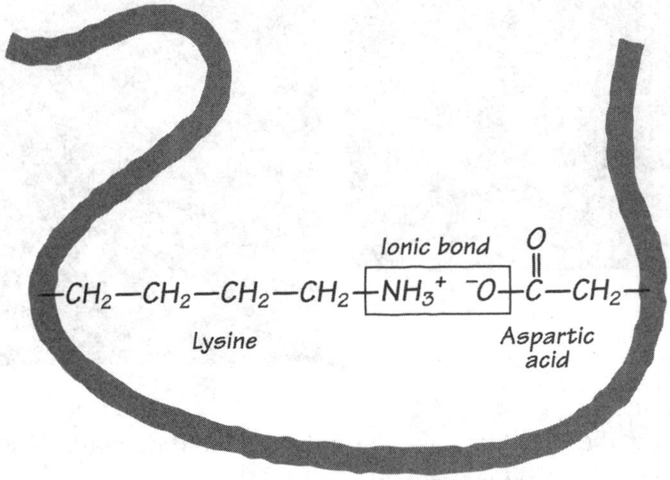

Ionic bond

$$-CH_2-CH_2-CH_2-CH_2-NH_3^+ \quad {}^-O-\overset{O}{\underset{\parallel}{C}}-CH_2-$$

Lysine

Aspartic acid

Name _____   Course/Section _____

Date _____   Professor/TA _____

Activity 3.2 What factors affect chemical reactions in cells?

Construct a concept map of general metabolism using the terms in the list below.

- Keep in mind that there are many ways to construct a concept map.
- Begin by writing each term on a separate Post-it note or piece of paper.
- Then organize the terms into a map that indicates how the terms are associated or related.
- Draw lines between terms, and add action phrases to the lines to indicate how the terms are related.
- If you are doing this activity in small groups in class, explain your map to another group when you finish it.

Here is an example:

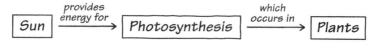

Terms

peptide bonds	activation energy	allosteric regulation
proteins	ΔG / free energy	activator
α-helix	endergonic	four-step enzyme-mediated
primary structure	exergonic	reaction sequence or
secondary structure	enzymes	metabolic pathway
tertiary structure	catalysts	(A⟶B⟶C⟶D)
β-pleated sheet	competitive inhibitor	intermediate
R-groups	noncompetitive	compound
hydrogen bonds	inhibitor	end-product
substrate or reactant	active site	feedback inhibition
(ligand)	product	

Use the understanding you gained from doing the concept map to answer the following questions.

1. Reduced organic compounds tend to contain stored energy in C–H bonds. As a general rule, the greater the number of C–H bonds, the greater the amount of potential energy stored in the molecule. Answer each question in the chart as it relates to the two reactions shown at the top. Be sure to explain the reasoning behind your answers.

	Reaction 1: $CH_4 + 2 O_2 \longrightarrow 2 H_2O + CO_2$ (methane)	Reaction 2: $6 CO_2 + 6 H_2O \longrightarrow$ $C_6H_{12}O_6 + 6 O_2$
a. Is the reaction exergonic or endergonic?		
b. Is the reaction spontaneous?		
c. Is the reaction anabolic or catabolic?		
d. Is ΔG (the change in free energy) positive or negative?		

2. All metabolic reactions in living organisms are enzyme mediated. Each enzyme is specific for one (or only a very few similar types of) reaction. Given this, there are approximately as many different kinds of enzymes as there are reactions.

    a. What characteristics do all enzymes share?

    b. What characteristics can differ among enzymes?

3. How can enzyme function be mediated or modified? To answer, complete columns a and b below.

a. What factors can modify enzyme function?	b. What effect(s) can each of these factors have on enzyme function?

    c. What role(s) can modification of enzyme function play in the cell?

Name _____   Course/Section _____

Date _____   Professor/TA _____

Activity 3.3 How can changes in experimental conditions affect enzyme-mediated reactions?

1. You set up a series of experiments to monitor the rates of a reaction. The reaction is an enzyme-mediated reaction in which A $\longrightarrow$ B + C. For each experiment in this series, you continuously add the reactant A and monitor its concentration so that the amount of A remains constant over time.

    For each group of experiments, explain how the differences in experimental conditions could affect the reaction.

    a. You compare two side-by-side experiments. In experiment 1, you use x amount of the enzyme. In experiment 2, you use $2x$ amount of the same enzyme.

    b. You compare two side-by-side experiments. In both you use equal amounts of the enzyme. In experiment 3, you allow the products to accumulate over time. In experiment 4, you remove the products from the system as they are produced.

    c. In the next two experiments, you use equal amounts of the enzyme. You run experiment 5 at 20°C and experiment 6 at 25°C.

    d. In two final experiments, you use equal amounts of the enzyme. You run experiment 7 at pH 6 and experiment 8 at pH 8.

2. Enzyme function can be inhibited or regulated by the presence of chemicals that mimic either the reactants or the products.

   a. How do competitive and noncompetitive inhibition of an enzyme differ?

   b. What are allosteric enzymes? What function(s) can they serve in reaction sequences?

3. An enzyme catalyzes the reaction $X \longrightarrow Y + Z$. In a series of experiments, it was found that substance A inhibits the enzyme.

   • When the concentration of X is high and A is low, the reaction proceeds rapidly and Y and Z are formed.
   • As the concentration of A increases, the reaction slows regardless of whether X is present in high or low concentration.
   • If the concentration of A is high (relative to X), the reaction stops.
   • If the concentration of A again decreases, the reaction will ultimately resume.

   What type of enzyme regulation is described here? Explain or justify your answer.

4. In an enzymatic pathway, A, B, and C are intermediates required to make D and 1, 2, and 3 are enzymes that catalyze the designated reactions:

$$
\begin{array}{ccccccc}
 & 1 & & 2 & & 3 & \\
A & \longrightarrow & B & \longrightarrow & C & \longrightarrow & D \\
\downarrow & & & & & & \\
E & & & & & &
\end{array}
$$

This is analogous to what happens in a factory. In a leather goods factory, for example, the leather (A) is cut into the parts needed for shoes (B). The shoe parts are sewn together (making C), and C is packaged for shipping as D. Now shoe sales are dropping and backpack sales (E) are increasing. As a result, the manager of the factory decides to switch production from shoes to backpacks.

a. Where should the shoe-making process be shut down—at step 1, 2, or 3? Explain.

b. In a cell, if an excess of a chemical product D arises, where should this synthetic pathway be shut down in the cell? Explain your reasoning.

c. What type(s) of enzyme regulation is/are most likely to occur in the cell in this type of feedback system? Explain your reasoning.

Activity 4.1 What makes a compound a nucleic acid?

1. Closely related macromolecules often have many characteristics in common. For example, they share many of the same chemical elements and functional groups. Therefore, to separate or distinguish closely related macromolecules, you need to determine how they differ and then target or label that difference.

   a. What makes RNA different from DNA?

   b. If you wanted to use a radioactive or fluorescent tag to label only the RNA in a cell and not the DNA, what compound(s) could you label that is/are specific for RNA?

   c. If you wanted to label only the DNA, what compound(s) could you label?

2. You want to use a radioactive tracer that will label only the protein in an RNA virus. Assume the virus is composed of only a protein coat and an RNA core. Which of the following would you use? Be sure to explain your answer.

   a. radioactive P   b. radioactive N   c. radioactive S   d. radioactive C

3. Watson and Crick used modeling to determine the structure of DNA. What information led them to determine the following?

   a. DNA is double stranded.

   b. The two strands of nucleotides in DNA run antiparallel.

   c. The nucleotides in the two antiparallel strands are arranged such that a purine is always paired with a pyrimidine.

4. For each nucleic acid strand shown below, indicate whether it is DNA or RNA, label each of the bases, and write out the nucleotide sequence, starting at the 5′ end. For assistance refer to Figure 4.1 on page 60 in *Biological Science*, 4th edition.

a. Type of nucleic acid:	b. Type of nucleic acid:
Nucleotide sequence as A, G, C, etc.:	Nucleotide sequence as A, G, C, etc.:
5′ — — — — 3′	5′ — — — — 3′

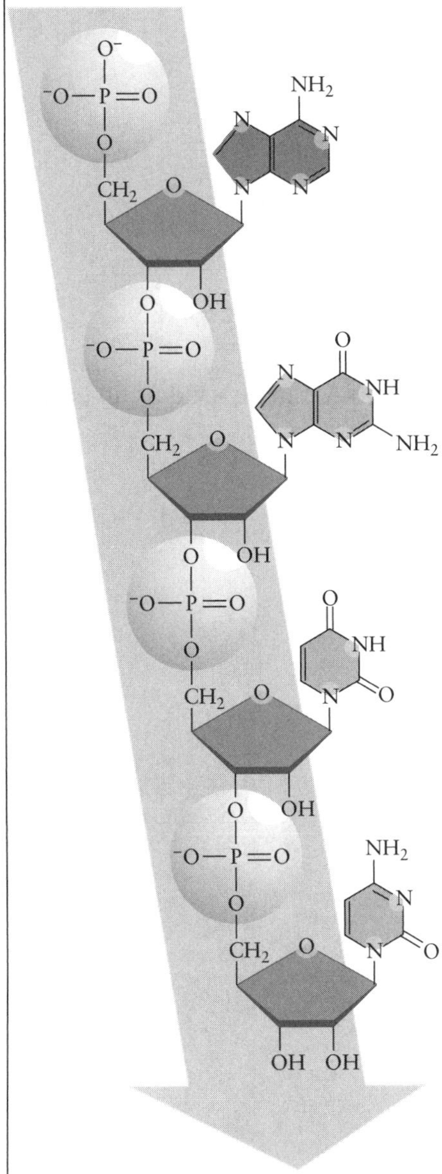

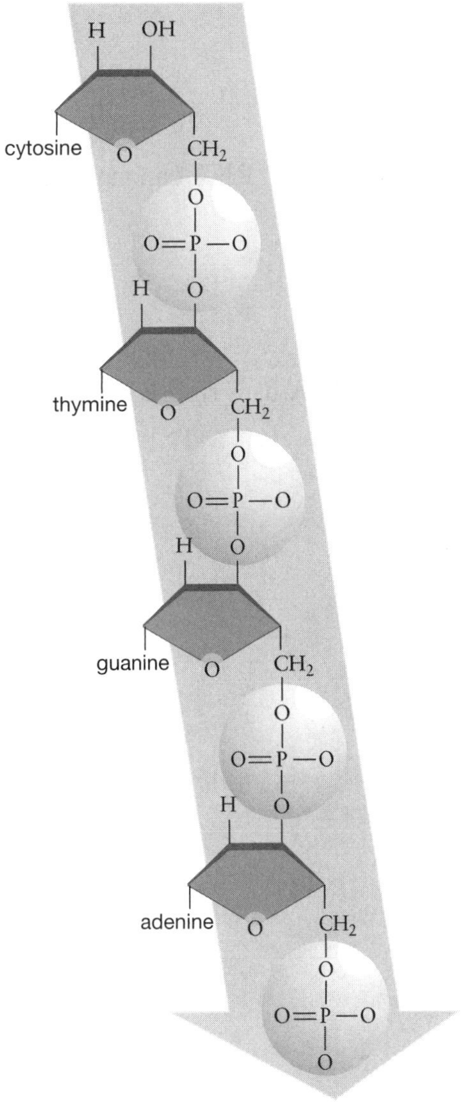

5. Many scientists believe that RNA molecules were the first macromolecules that emerged to allow some of the fundamental processes of life to be conducted. Indicate which of the following statements supports the RNA world hypothesis, and be sure to justify your answer.

   a. RNA includes the base uracil (U) instead of thymidine (T).

   b. DNA is more stable than RNA.

   c. Unlike DNA, RNA can catalyze chemical reactions.

   d. Since RNA uses ribose instead of deoxyribose, RNA can be used as an energy source.

Name ——————————————   Course/Section ——————————————

Date ——————————————   Professor/TA ——————————————

 Activity 5.1 How does structure affect function in carbohydrates?

1. Polysaccharides, complex carbohydrates, have a wide range of structures that affect
    how these macromolecules can function in organisms. Fill out the chart below to
    help you understand the characteristics of different polysaccharide structures and the
    roles they play in living organisms. (Refer to Summary Table 5.1 on page 75 of
    Biological Science, 4th edition.)

	Structural components	3-D Structural arrangement	Role(s) the polysaccharide play(s) in organisms	Type(s) of organisms in which compound is found
Starch				
Glycogen				
Cellulose				

Chitin				
Peptidoglycan				

2. Compare the structures of starch and glycogen. Compare the structures of cellulose, chitin, and peptidoglycan. How are each of these suited to their functions?

Name ————————————— Course/Section —————————————

Date ————————————— Professor/TA —————————————

Activity 6.1 What roles do lipids play in organisms?

1. Fill out the chart below to help you understand the characteristics of different types of lipids and the roles they play in living organisms.

	Molecular components	Molecular arrangement	Role(s) the lipid plays in an organism
Steroid			
Phospholipid			
Fat			

2. Lipids as a group are defined as being hydrophobic, or insoluble in water. As a result, this group includes a fairly wide range of compounds—for example, fats, oils, waxes, and steroids like cholesterol.

   a. How are fatty acids and glycerol linked together to form fats (triglycerides)?

   b. How do phospholipids differ from triglycerides?

   c. How are the structures of steroids, phospholipids, and fats suited to their different functions?

3. You have a friend who lost 20 pounds of fat on a diet. Where did the fat go (how was it lost)? Be sure to explain your reasoning.

Name —————————————   Course/Section ——————————————

Date ——————————————   Professor/TA ——————————————

 Activity 6.2 What controls the movement of materials into and out of the cell?

1. To be alive, most cells must maintain a relatively constant internal environment. To do this, they must be able to control the movement of materials into and out of the cell.

    What characteristics of the cell membrane determine what gets into the cell and what doesn't? That is, what determines the permeability of a cell or organelle membrane?

    To answer these questions, first consider the answers to the following questions:

a. If a cell membrane were composed of only a phospholipid bilayer, what properties would it have?	b. What different roles or functions do membrane proteins serve?	c. Why are some cells types more permeable to a substance (for example, sodium ions) than others?

Using your understanding of the answers in a–c, now answer these questions: What characteristics of the cell membrane determine what gets into the cell and what doesn't? That is, what determines the permeability of a cell or organelle membrane?

2. You design an experiment to test the effect(s) various compounds have on the osmotic potential of a model cell. You know that substances dissolved in aqueous or gaseous solutions tend to diffuse from regions of higher concentration to regions of lower concentration.

You fill each of three (20 ml) dialysis bags half full with one of these substances:

- 5% by weight of glucose in distilled water
- 5% by weight of egg albumin (protein) in distilled water
- 5% by weight of glass bead (one glass bead) in distilled water

The dialysis bag is permeable to water but impermeable to glucose, albumin, and glass bead.

   a. If the final weight of each bag is 10 g, how many grams of glucose, albumin, and glass bead were added to each bag?

   b. The molecular weight of the protein is about 45,000 atomic mass units, and the molecular weight of glucose is about 180 atomic mass units. How can you estimate the number of molecules of glucose in the 5% solution compared to the number of albumin molecules in its 5% solution?

   c. You put the dialysis bags into three separate flasks of distilled water. After 2 hours, you remove the bags and record these weights:

Dialysis bag	Weight
Glucose	13.2 g
Albumin	10.1 g
Glass bead	10.0 g

How do you explain these results? (*Hint:* Consider the surface area-to-volume ratio of each of the three substances and review pages 23 and 24 of *Biological Science*, 4th edition.)

   d. What results would you predict if you set up a similar experiment but used 5% glucose and 5% sucrose?

Name ——————————————   Course/Section ——————————————

Date ——————————————   Professor/TA ——————————————

 ### Activity 6.3 How is the structure of a cell membrane related to its function?

Membranes compartmentalize the different functions of living cells. The cell membrane is a barrier between the cell or organism and its environment. Similarly, within the cell, membranes of organelles separate the different reactions of metabolism from each other. Use the supplies provided in class or devise your own at home to develop a model of a cell membrane. Developing models of systems can help you understand their overall structure as well as their function(s).

Building the Model

- Include in the membrane the phospholipid bilayer (phosphate heads and fatty-acid tails) as well as the integral proteins.
- Design integral proteins that serve the functions of facilitated diffusion and active transport.
- Indicate how the various types of integral proteins might differ in structure and operation.

Use the understanding you gain from your model to answer the questions on the next pages.

1. Substances can move across the membrane via simple diffusion, facilitated diffusion, or active transport.

	a. Where does it occur in membrane?	b. Does it require transport protein?	c. Does it require input of energy?
Simple diffusion			
Facilitated diffusion			
Active transport			

d. What functions might each of the three types of diffusion serve in an independent cell like a *Paramecium* or an amoeba?

e. What functions might each of the three types of diffusion serve in a multicellular organism—for example, a human or a tree?

2. What would you need to observe or measure to determine whether a substance was moved across a membrane via each type of diffusion?

Simple diffusion	Facilitated diffusion	Active transport

3. The ratios of saturated to unsaturated phospholipids in an organism's membranes can change in response to changes in environmental conditions.

a. How do the properties of a membrane that contains a low percentage of unsaturated phospholipids compare with those of a membrane that contains a high percentage of unsaturated phospholipids?

b. Considering what you know about the properties of saturated and unsaturated fatty acids, would you expect an amoeba that lives in a pond in a cold northern climate to have a higher or lower percentage of saturated fatty acids in its membranes during the summer as compared to the winter? Explain your answer.

4. A fish is removed from a contaminated lake. You determine that a particular toxin is present in its cells at concentration A = 1500 μg/L. You place the fish in a tank full of clean water (A = 0 μg/L), and several days later you measure the toxin concentration in the cells (level B).

a. On the graphs below, predict how the toxin concentrations in the fish and in the water will change over time if:
(i) The toxin is water soluble.
(ii) The toxin is fat soluble.

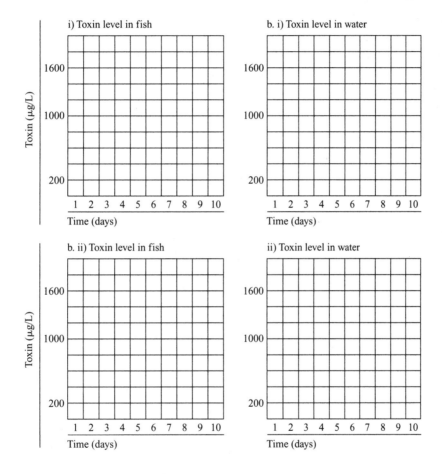

i) Toxin level in fish

Toxin (μg/L)

1600

1000

200

1 2 3 4 5 6 7 8 9 10
Time (days)

b. i) Toxin level in water

1600

1000

200

1 2 3 4 5 6 7 8 9 10
Time (days)

b. ii) Toxin level in fish

Toxin (μg/L)

1600

1000

200

1 2 3 4 5 6 7 8 9 10
Time (days)

ii) Toxin level in water

1600

1000

200

1 2 3 4 5 6 7 8 9 10
Time (days)

b. After making your hypothesis, you test it by measuring the toxin levels in the fish at various times during its several days in the tank. You observe that the level of toxin drops in the fish from 1500 µg/L to 750 µg/L and then stabilizes at 750µg/L . You test the water in the tank and find that after it stabilizes, toxin is present in the water at concentration 750 µg/L also.

- Which of your predictions fit these data?
- Which of the following processes is most likely eliminating the toxin from the fish?
  - (i)   passive transport
  - (ii) first active, then passive transport
  - (iii) first passive, then active transport
  - (iv) active transport

c. Given the situation in part b, what should you do, in the short term, to continue to reduce the toxin level in the fish below 750 µg/L?

Name —————————————   Course/Section ————————————————

Date —————————————   Professor/TA ——————————————————

Activity 6.4 Effects of missing or non-functional ion channels in cell membranes

- Cystic fibrosis transmembrane conductance regulator (CFTR) proteins function in cell membranes to allow chloride ions across cell membranes. Individuals with cystic fibrosis (CF) have abnormal CFTR proteins that do not allow Cl^- to move across cell membranes. Chloride channels are essential to maintain osmotic balance inside cells. Without properly functioning Cl^- channels, water builds up inside the cell. One result is a thickening of mucus in lungs and air passages.

You are doing research on a disease, and you hypothesize that there is a defect in an ion channel of the cell membrane, similar to the defect in the CFTR protein in individuals with CF. Diagram or model the production of a normal membrane ion channel. Based on your understanding of ion channel functions, propose at least three different alterations that could result in a nonfunctional or missing ion channel. What questions would you need to answer to determine which of these may be correct?

Extend Your
Understanding **Activity 6.5 What effect does cholesterol have on
phospholipid membrane permeability?**

Figure 6.11 on page 88 of your textbook shows the results of an experiment designed to
test whether cholesterol within a phospholipid bilayer has an effect on membrane
permeability. If the results were different, as shown in the graph below, how would the
conclusion change? What additional questions would you ask, or what experiments would
you propose, to better understand the relationship between membrane composition,
permeability to glycerol, and temperature?

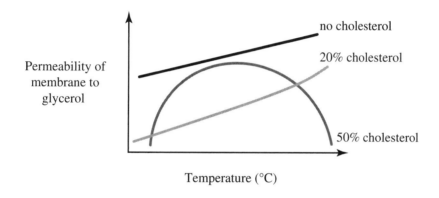

Name ——————————— Course/Section ———————————

Date ——————————— Professor/TA ———————————

Chapters 3–6 What do carbohydrates, lipids, proteins, and nucleic acids have in common? How are they different?

Refer to the figure (Some Simple Chemistry) on the next page when doing this activity.

Part A. Answer the questions. Then use your answers to develop simple rules for identifying carbohydrates, lipids, proteins, and nucleic acids.

1. What is the approximate C:H:O ratio in each of the following types of macromolecules?

Carbohydrates	Lipids	Proteins	Nucleic acids

2. Which of the compounds listed in question 1 can often be composed of C, H, and O alone?

3. Which of the compounds can be identified by looking at the C:H:O ratios alone?

Some Simple Chemistry

Compound	Basic components	➡ Reaction ➡	Product

Carbohydrates:

Sugars, starches,
glycogen,
cellulose

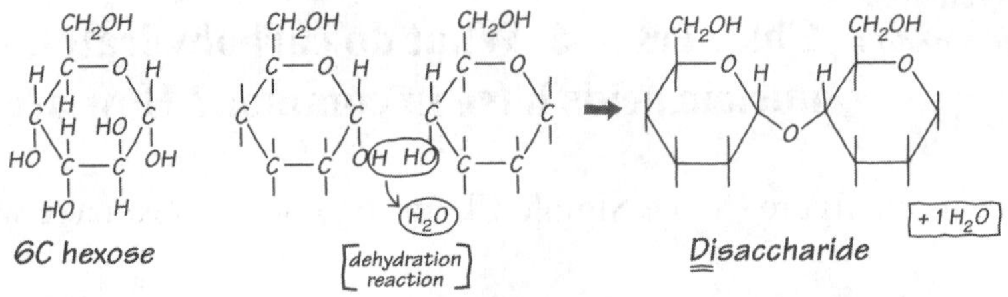

CH_2OH ... 6C hexose

dehydration reaction

H_2O

$+1 H_2O$

Disaccharide

Lipids:

Fats, oils,
waxes,
cholesterol

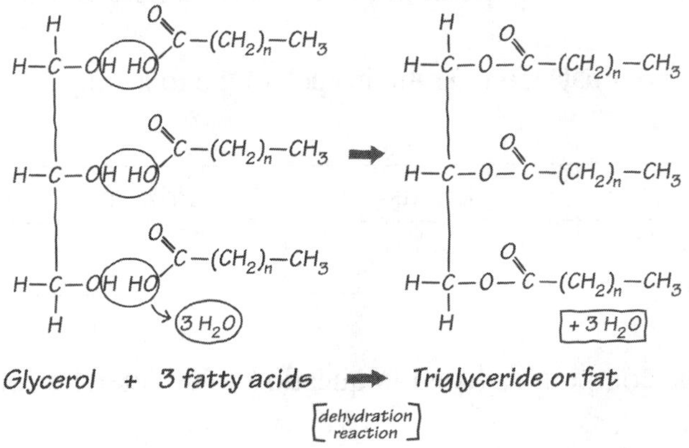

$3 H_2O$

$+ 3 H_2O$

Glycerol + 3 fatty acids ➡ Triglyceride or fat

[dehydration reaction]

Proteins:

Enzymes,
structural
proteins

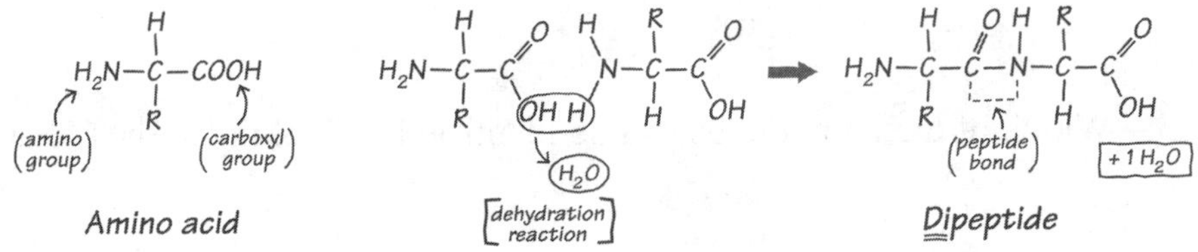

$H_2N-C-COOH$

(amino group)   (carboxyl group)

Amino acid

H_2O

[dehydration reaction]

(peptide bond)

$+1 H_2O$

Dipeptide

Nucleic acids:

DNA,
RNA

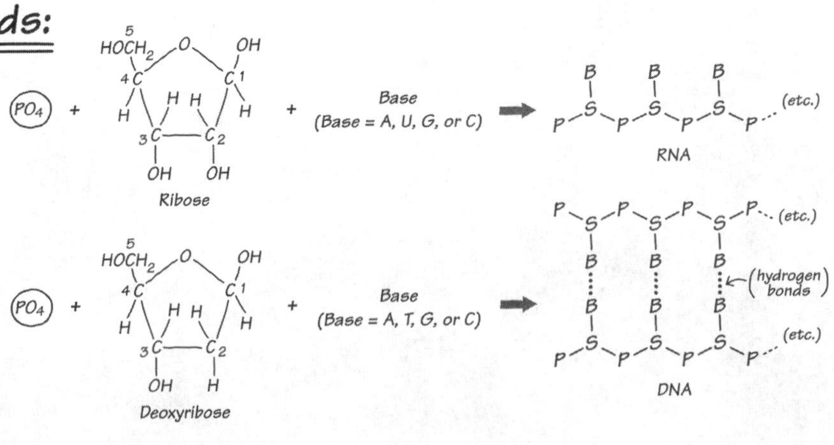

PO_4 +

$HOCH_2$ ... Ribose

+ Base
(Base = A, U, G, or C) ➡

B   B   B
P–S–P–S–P–S–P··· (etc.)

RNA

PO_4 +

$HOCH_2$ ... Deoxyribose

+ Base
(Base = A, T, G, or C) ➡

P–S–P–S–P–S–P···(etc.)
B   B   B
(hydrogen bonds)
B   B   B
P–S–P–S–P–S–P···(etc.)

DNA

4. What other elements are commonly associated with each of these four types of macromolecules?

	Carbohydrates	Lipids	Proteins	Nucleic acids
Always contain P				
Generally contain no P				
Always contain N				
Generally contain no N				
Frequently contain S				
Generally contain no S				

5. Based on your answers to questions 1–4 and what you learned from Chapters 3–6 in *Biological Science,* 4th edition, what simple rule(s) can you use to identify the following macromolecules?

Macromolecule	How to identify
nucleic acids	
DNA versus RNA	
proteins	
carbohydrates	
lipids	

Part B. Carbohydrate, lipid, protein, or nucleic acid? Name that structure!

Based on the rules you developed in Part A, identify the compounds below (and on the following page) as carbohydrates, lipids, amino acids, polypeptides, or nucleic acids. In addition, indicate whether each is likely to be polar or nonpolar, hydrophilic or hydrophobic.

1) $C_{17}H_{35}COOH$ +

$$
\begin{array}{c}
\quad\quad\quad\quad H \\
H-O-C-H \\
\quad\quad | \\
H-O-C-H \\
\quad\quad | \\
H-O-C-H
\end{array}
\longrightarrow
\begin{array}{c}
\quad\quad\quad\quad\quad H \\
C_{17}H_{35}COO-C-H \\
\quad\quad\quad\quad | \\
C_{17}H_{35}COO-C-H \\
\quad\quad\quad\quad | \\
C_{17}H_{35}COO-C-H
\end{array}
$$

2)

$$
HC = C - CH_2\overset{\overset{\textstyle H}{|}}{C} - COOH
$$

with NH_2 on the carbon, ring closed by $H^{\pm}-N$ and N with C and H.

3)

$$
\underset{HO}{\overset{O}{\|}}C - \underset{H}{\overset{H}{C}} - \underset{H}{N} - \overset{O}{\underset{}{\|}}C - \overset{OH}{\underset{}{\overset{|}{C}HCH_3}}C - N - \overset{O}{\underset{}{\|}}C - \overset{CH_2}{\underset{}{C}} - \overset{H}{\underset{H}{N}}
$$

4)

$$
NH_2 - \overset{NH_2}{\overset{\|}{C}} - NH - CH_2 - CH_2 - CH_2 - \underset{\underset{H}{\overset{|}{N}-H}}{CH} - \overset{O}{\underset{OH}{\overset{\|}{C}}}
$$

5)

$$
\begin{array}{cccc}
CH_2OH & CH_2OH & CH_2OH & CH_2OH
\end{array}
$$
(four ring sugar units linked by O bridges, with OH groups)

6)

$$
H - \overset{H}{\underset{OH}{C}} - \overset{H}{\underset{OH}{C}} - \overset{H}{\underset{OH}{C}} - \overset{H}{\underset{OH}{C}} - \overset{H}{\underset{O}{C}}
$$

7)

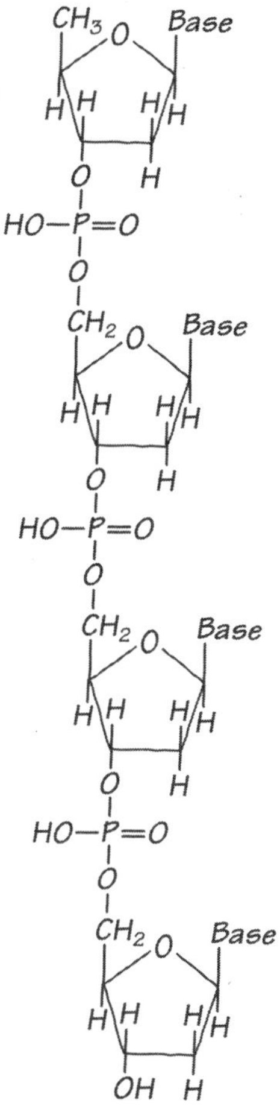

8)

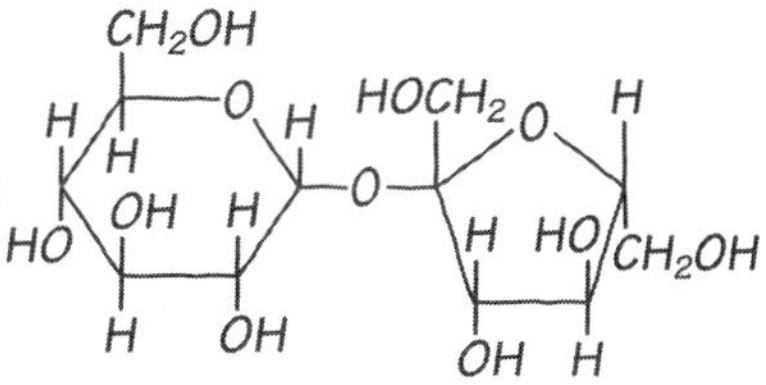

9) $H_3C-CH_2-CH_2-CH_2-CH_2-CH_2-CH_2-CH_2-CH_2-C\overset{\displaystyle O}{\underset{\displaystyle OH}{}}$

10)

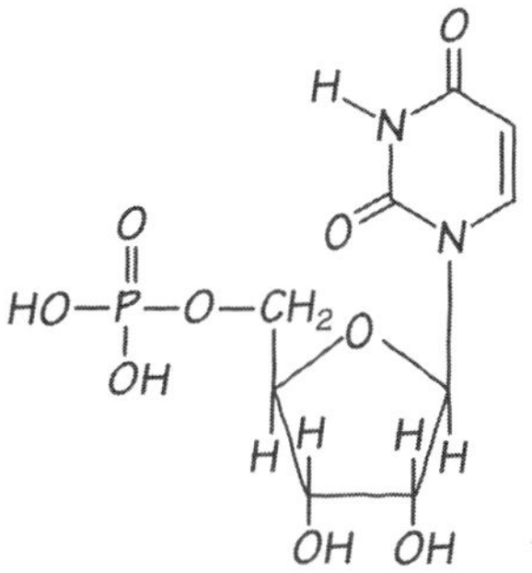

Part C. Thought Questions

1. Given your understanding of energy storage in organic macromolecules, explain why carbohydrates and proteins have 4 calories/gram, but fats have 9 calories/gram, as shown on the nutrition information of all food packaging.

2. While on a safari in the jungle, your friend was bitten by a large spider. He nearly died from hemolysis, or breakage of many of his red blood cells. You analyzed the spider venom and found three enzymes: phospholipase, which degrades phospholipids; neuraminidase, which removes cell-surface carbohydrates; and protease, which degrades proteins. Which of these enzymes do you think was responsible for his near fatal red blood cell hemolysis? Why?

Name —————————————— Course/Section ——————————————

Part D. Process of Science

A student, Mary, is given four samples and told they are lysine (an amino acid), lactose (a disaccharide), insulin (a protein hormone), and RNA. The samples are in test tubes marked 1, 2, 3 and 4, but Mary doesn't know which compound is in which tube. She is instructed to identify the contents of each tube.

a. In her first test, she tries to hydrolyze a portion of the contents of each tube. Hydrolysis occurs in all tubes, except tube 3.

b. In Mary's next test, she finds that tubes 1, 2, and 3 are positive for nitrogen, but only tube 2 gives a positive result when tested for the presence of sulfur.

c. The last test Mary performs shows that the compound in tube 1 contains a high percentage of phosphate.

Based on these data, fill in the following table and explain your answers.

Tube number	Contents	Explanation
1		
2		
3		
4		

Use your understanding of the chemical characteristics of the four major types of macromolecules in living organisms to predict the outcome of the following experiments. Be sure to explain your reasoning.

Part D (*continued*). **Experiment a:** You stir 10 g of glucose and 10 ml of phospholipids in a 500-ml beaker that contains 200 ml of distilled water. Draw a diagram to show where and how the glucose and phospholipids would be distributed after you let the mixture settle for about 30 minutes.

Experiment b: You do Experiment a again, but this time you stir 10 g of glucose and 10 ml of phospholipids in a different 500-ml beaker that contains 200 ml of distilled water and 100 ml of oil. Draw a diagram to show where and how the glucose, phospholipids, and oil would be distributed after you let the solution settle for about 30 minutes.

Experiment c: To completely fill a sealed 500-ml glass container that contains 490 ml of distilled water, you inject 10 ml of phospholipids into it. (A small gasket allows the air to leave as you inject the phospholipids.) You shake this mixture vigorously and then let it settle for an hour or more. Draw a diagram to show how the phospholipids would be distributed in the container.

Activity 7.1 What makes a cell a living organism?

1. Single-celled organisms and individual cells within multicellular organisms can vary greatly in appearance as well as in the functions they perform. Nonetheless, each of these cells is alive and therefore must have some common characteristics.

a. At a minimum, what structures or components must a cell contain to be alive?	b. What is the function of each structure or component listed in part a?

   c. If you consider the types of single-celled organisms that exist today, which, if any, have a structure similar to your description in part a?

2. What would you need to add to or change about the cell you described in question 1 to make it:

a. A eukaryotic animal cell?	b. A eukaryotic plant cell?

3. To get an idea of the different sizes of various cellular components, do the following calculations: Assume that the cell, its nucleus, and a globular protein—for example, an enzyme—are spherical. In addition, assume the diameter of the protein is 5 nm, the diameter of the cell is 100 μm (micrometers), and the diameter of the nucleus is 40 μm.

If you draw the globular protein as a sphere with a diameter of 2 cm (approximately the diameter of a U.S. penny), what size would each of the following measurements of the cell be if drawn to the same scale (5 nm real length = 2 cm)?	
a. The radius of a microtubule (Refer to Summary Table 7.3 in *Biological Science*, 4th ed.)	
b. The diameter of the nucleus	
c. The diameter of the cell	
d. The volume ($V = 4/3\ \pi r^3$) of the protein 1 nanometer cubed ($1\ nm^3$) $= 1.0 \times 10^{-21}$ centimeters cubed (cm^3).	
e. The volume of the nucleus	
f. The volume of the cell	

g. The volume of the Empire State Building is $1.05 \times 10^6\ m^3$. How many of your scaled nuclei could fit into the Empire State Building? How many of your scaled cells could fit?

h. Do the results of these calculations help you to understand how so much can be going on inside a cell at once? Explain.

Name _____   Course/Section _____

Date _____   Professor/TA _____

Activity 8.1 How are chemical signals translated into cellular responses?

Chapter 8 in *Biological Science*, 4th edition, describes at least four types of signal receptors. Three of these—G-protein-linked receptors, tyrosine-kinase receptors, and ion-channel receptors—are plasma membrane proteins. Protein receptors found in the cytoplasm, or nucleus, of the cell are the fourth type. Some signals (for example, a protein hormone) interact with signal receptors in the cell membrane to initiate the process of signal transduction. This often involves changes in a series of different relay molecules in a signal transduction pathway. Ultimately, the transduced signal initiates an intracellular response. Other types of signals (for example, steroid hormones) can diffuse through the cell membrane and interact with intracellular receptors. For example, testosterone interacts with its receptor in the cell's cytoplasm, enters the nucleus, and causes the transcription of specific genes.

To help you understand how signal transduction occurs in cells, develop dynamic (claymation-type) models of both a G-protein receptor system and a tyrosine-kinase receptor system. Use playdough or cut out pieces of paper to represent all the structural components and molecules listed here under each system.

G-protein receptor system

signal protein

G-protein-linked receptor

plasma membrane

inactive and active G protein

GTP and GDP

inactive and active enzyme

signal transduction pathway

Tyrosine-kinase receptor system

signal protein

tyrosine-kinase receptor

plasma membrane

inactive and active relay proteins

ATP and ADP

signal transduction pathway

Use your models to show how signal reception by each of the systems can lead to the release of Ca^{2+} from the endoplasmic reticulum. Demonstrate and explain your models to another student group or to your instructor.

Use your models and the information in Chapter 8 of your textbook to answer the questions on the next page.

1. How are these two systems similar? Consider both structural similarities and similarities in how the systems function.

2. How are the two systems different? Consider both structural differences and differences in how the systems function.

3. Both systems can generate elaborate multistep signal transduction pathways. These pathways can greatly amplify the cell's response to a signal; the more steps in the pathway, the greater the amplification of the signal. Explain how this amplification can occur. (Review Figure 8.14 on page 141 in your textbook.)

Name _____   Course/Section _____

Date _____   Professor/TA _____

Integrate Your
Understanding **Activity 9.1 A Quick Review of Energy**
                                        Transformations

Review pages 27–30 of Chapter 2 and pages 157–161 of Chapter 9 in *Biological*
Science, **4th edition. Then complete the following discussion by either filling in the**
blank or circling the appropriate term.

To maintain life, organisms must be able to convert energy from one form to another. For example, in the process of photosynthesis, algae, plants, and photosynthetic prokaryotes use the energy from sunlight to convert carbon dioxide and water to glucose and oxygen (a waste product).

The summary reaction for photosynthesis can be written as

$$6\,CO_2 + 6\,H_2O \longrightarrow C_6H_{12}O_6 + 6\,O_2$$

This type of reaction is an oxidation–reduction (or redox) reaction. This reaction is also **[anabolic/catabolic]** and **[endergonic/exergonic]**.

In redox reactions, _____ (and associated H^+ ions) are transferred from one compound or element to another. If one compound or element loses _____ and becomes oxidized, another must gain _____ and become reduced. For example, in photosynthesis, water becomes **[oxidized/reduced]** (to O_2) and the _____ (and associated H^+ ions) it "loses" in the process **[oxidize/reduce]**
CO_2 to glucose.

[Anabolic/Catabolic] reactions "build" more complex molecules from simpler ones. To do this they require energy input. Reactions that require the input of energy are termed **[endergonic/exergonic]** reactions.

The reactions involved in aerobic respiration are also redox reactions:

$$C_6H_{12}O_6 + 6\,O_2 \longrightarrow 6\,CO_2 + 6\,H_2O$$

In this set of reactions, however, more complex molecules are "broken down" into simpler ones. Glucose is broken down or becomes **[oxidized/reduced]** (to CO_2), and the oxygen becomes **[oxidized/reduced]** (to water).

[**Anabolic/Catabolic**] reactions break down more complex molecules into simpler ones and in the process release energy. Reactions that release energy that can be used to do work are [**endergonic/exergonic**]. Therefore, aerobic respiration is a(n) [**anabolic/catabolic**] process and is [**endergonic/exergonic**].

[**Endergonic/Exergonic**] reactions are also said to be spontaneous reactions. Does this mean that if we don't keep glucose in tightly sealed containers it will spontaneously interact with atmospheric oxygen and turn into carbon dioxide and water? The answer is obviously no.

Spontaneous reactions rarely occur "spontaneously" because all chemical reactions, even those that release energy, require some addition of energy—the energy of activation— before they can occur. One way of supplying this energy is to add heat. An example is heating a marshmallow over a flame or campfire. When enough heat is added to reach (or overcome) the activation energy, the sugar in the marshmallow reacts by oxidizing. (Burning is a form of oxidation.) The marshmallow will continue to burn even if you remove it from the campfire. As the marshmallow burns, carbon dioxide and water are formed as products of the reaction, and the energy that was stored in the bonds of the sugar is released as heat.

If our cells used heat to overcome activation energies in metabolism, they would probably burn up like the marshmallow did. Instead, living systems use protein catalysts or enzymes to lower the energy of activation without adding heat. In addition, the metabolic breakdown of sugars is carried out in a controlled series of reactions. At each step or reaction in the sequence, a small amount of the total energy is released. Some of this energy is still lost as heat. The rest is converted to other forms that can be used in the cell to drive or fuel coupled endergonic reactions or to make ATP.

Name _____   Course/Section _____

Date _____   Professor/TA _____

 Activity 9.2 Modeling Cellular Respiration: How can cells convert the energy in glucose to ATP?

Using your textbook, lecture notes, and the materials available in class (or those you devise at home), model both fermentation (an anaerobic process) and cellular respiration (an aerobic process) as they occur in a plant or animal cell. Each model should be a dynamic (working or active) representation of the events that occur in glycolysis.

Building the Model

- Use chalk on a tabletop, or a marker on a large sheet of paper, to draw the cell membrane and the mitochondrial membranes.
- Use playdough or cut out pieces of paper to represent the molecules, ions, and membrane transporters or pumps.
- Use the pieces you assembled to model the processes of fermentation and aerobic respiration. Develop a dynamic (claymation-type) model that allows you to manipulate or move glucose and its breakdown products through the various steps of both fermentation and aerobic respiration.
- When you feel you have developed a good working model, demonstrate and explain it to another student or to your instructor.

Be sure your model of **fermentation** includes and explains the actions and roles of the following:

glycolysis	ADP
cytoplasm	P_i
electrons	ATP
protons	pyruvate
glucose	ethyl alcohol (or lactic acid)
NAD^+	substrate-level phosphorylation
NADH	

Be sure your model of **cellular respiration** includes and explains the actions and roles of the following:

glucose	electron transport chain
oxygen	mitochondria
carbon dioxide	inner mitochondrial membrane
pyruvate	outer mitochondrial membrane
acetyl CoA	H^+
NAD^+	electrons (e^-)
NADH	chemiosmosis
FAD	ATP synthase (proton pumps)
$FADH_2$	cristae
ADP	proton gradients
P_i	oxidative phosphorylation
ATP	substrate-level phosphorylation
water	oxidative phosphorylation

Use your models and the information in Chapter 9 of *Biological Science*, 4th edition, to answer these questions.

1. The summary formula for cellular respiration is

$$C_6H_{12}O_6 + 6\,O_2 \longrightarrow 6\,CO_2 + 6\,H_2O + Energy$$

a. Where is each of the reactants used in the overall process?	b. Where is each of the products produced in the overall process?
$C_6H_{12}O_6$ + 6 O_2 $\longrightarrow$ 6 CO_2 + 6 H_2O + Energy	

2. In cellular respiration, the oxidation of glucose is carried out in a controlled series of reactions. At each step or reaction in the sequence, a small amount of the total energy is released. Some of this energy is lost as heat. The rest is converted to other forms that can be used by the cell to drive or fuel coupled endergonic reactions or to make ATP.

a. What is/are the overall function(s) of glycolysis?	b. What is/are the overall function(s) of the Krebs cycle?	c. What is/are the overall function(s) of oxidative phosphorylation?

3. Are the compounds listed here *used* or *produced* in:

	Glycolysis?	The Krebs cycle?	Oxidative phosphorylation?
Glucose			
O_2			
CO_2			
H_2O			
ATP			
$ADP + P_i$			
NADH			
NAD^+			

4. The cell's supply of ADP, P_i, and NAD^+ is finite (limited). What happens to cellular respiration when all of the cell's NAD^+ has been converted to NADH?

5. If the Krebs cycle does not require oxygen, why does cellular respiration stop after glycolysis when no oxygen is present?

6. Many organisms can withstand periods of oxygen debt (anaerobic conditions). Yeast undergoing oxygen debt converts pyruvic acid to ethanol and carbon dioxide. Animals undergoing oxygen debt convert pyruvic acid to lactic acid. Pyruvic acid is fairly nontoxic in even high concentrations. Both ethanol and lactic acid are toxic in even moderate concentrations. Explain why this conversion occurs in organisms.

7. How efficient is fermentation? How efficient is cellular respiration? Remember that efficiency is the amount of useful energy (as ATP) gained during the process divided by the total amount of energy available in glucose. Use 686 kcal as the total energy available in 1 mol of glucose and 8 kcal as the energy available in 1 mol of ATP.

Efficiency of fermentation	Efficiency of aerobic respiration

8. a. Why can't cells store large quantities of ATP? (*Hint:* Consider both the chemical stability of the molecule and the cell's osmotic potential.)

   b. Given that cells can't store ATP for long periods of time, how do they store energy?

   c. What are the advantages of storing energy in these alternate forms?

9. To make a 5 *M* solution of hydrochloric acid, we add 400 ml of 12.5 *M* hydrochloric acid to 600 ml of distilled water. Before adding the acid, however, we place the flask containing the distilled water into the sink because this solution can heat up so rapidly that the flask breaks. How is this reaction similar to what happens in chemiosmosis? How is it different?

Similarities	Differences

Name _____   Course/Section _____

Date _____   Professor/TA _____

Extend Your
Understanding **Activity 9.3 Cell Respiration—Experimental scenarios**

a. If it takes 1000 g of glucose to grow 10 g of an anaerobic bacterium, how many grams of glucose would it take to grow 10 g of that same bacterium if it was respiring aerobically? Estimate your answer. For example, if it takes X amount of glucose to grow 10 g of anaerobic bacteria, what factor would you have to multiply or divide X by to grow 10 g of the same bacteria aerobically? Explain how you arrived at your answer.

b. Mitochondria isolated from liver cells can be used to study the rate of electron transport in response to a variety of chemicals. The rate of electron transport is measured as the rate of disappearance of O_2 from the solution using an oxygen-sensitive electrode.

How can we justify using the disappearance of oxygen from the solution as a measure of electron transport?

c. Humans oxidize glucose in the presence of oxygen. For each mole of glucose oxidized, about 686 kcal of energy is released. This is true whether the mole of glucose is oxidized in human cells or burned in the air. A calorie is the amount of energy required to raise the temperature of 1 g of water by 1°C; 686 kcal = 686,000 cal. The average human requires about 2000 kcal of energy per day, which is equivalent to about 3 mol of glucose per day. Given this, why don't humans spontaneously combust?

d. A gene has recently been identified that encodes for a protein that increases longevity in mice. To function in increasing longevity, this gene requires a high ratio of $NAD^+/NADH$. Researchers have used this as evidence in support of a "caloric restriction" hypothesis for longevity—that a decrease in total calorie intake increases longevity. How does the requirement for a high $NAD^+/NADH$ ratio support the caloric restriction hypothesis?

e. An active college age athlete can burn more than 3000 kcal/day in exercise.
   *   If conversion of one mole of ATP to ADP + P_i releases about 7.3 kcal, roughly speaking, how many moles of ATP need to be produced per day in order for this energy need to be met?
   *   If the molecular weight of ATP is 573, how much would the required ATP weigh in kilograms?
   *   Explain these results.

Activity 10.1 Modeling Photosynthesis: How can cells use the sun's energy to convert carbon dioxide and water into glucose?

Activity 10.1 is designed to help you understand

1. The roles photosystems I and II and the Calvin cycle play in photosynthesis

2. How and why C_4 and CAM photosynthesis differ from C_3 photosynthesis

Using your textbook, lecture notes, and the materials available in class (or those you devise at home), model photosynthesis as it occurs in a plant cell. Your model should be a dynamic (working or active) representation of the events that occur in the various phases of C_3 photosynthesis.

Building the Model

- Use chalk on a tabletop, or a marker on a large sheet of paper, to draw the cell membrane and the chloroplast membranes.
- Use playdough or cut out pieces of paper to represent the molecules, ions, and membrane transporters or pumps.
- Use the pieces you assembled to model the processes involved in C_3 photosynthesis. Develop a dynamic (claymation-type) model that allows you to manipulate or move carbon dioxide and water and its breakdown products through the various steps of the process.
- When you feel you have developed a good working model, demonstrate and explain it to another student or to your instructor.

Your model of C_3 photosynthesis should include what occurs in photosystems I and II and in the Calvin cycle. For **photosystems I and II**, be sure your model includes and explains the roles of the following:

$NADP^+$	H^+
NADPH	e^-
ADP	chemiosmosis
P_i	ATP synthase
ATP	e^- carriers in thylakoid membranes
water and oxygen	

Also indicate where in the plant cell each item is required or produced.

For the Calvin cycle, be sure your model includes and explains the roles of the following:

> glucose
> C_3 or three-carbon sugars
> carbon dioxide
> NADPH
> ATP

Also indicate where in the plant cell each item is required or produced.

After you've modeled C_3 photosynthesis, indicate how the system would be altered for C_4 and CAM photosynthesis.

- Indicate where in the cells of the leaf PEP carboxylase exists and how it reacts to capture CO_2. Be sure to indicate the fate of the captured CO_2.
- Do the same for PEP carboxylase in CAM plants.

Use your model and the information in Chapter 10 of *Biological Science*, 4th edition, to answer these questions.

1. The various reactions in photosynthesis are spatially segregated from each other within the chloroplast. Draw a simplified diagram of a chloroplast and include these parts: outer membrane, grana, thylakoid, lumen, stroma/matrix.

a. Where in the chloroplast do the light reactions occur?	
b. Where in the chloroplast is the chemiosmotic gradient developed?	
c. Where in the chloroplast does the Calvin cycle occur?	

2. In photosynthesis, the reduction of carbon dioxide to form glucose is carried out in a controlled series of reactions. In general, each step or reaction in the sequence requires the input of energy. The Sun is the ultimate source of this energy.

a. What is/are the overall function(s) of photosystem I?	b. What is/are the overall function(s) of photosystem II?	c. What is/are the overall function(s) of the Calvin cycle?

3. Are the compounds listed here *used* or *produced* in:	Photosystem I?	Photosystem II?	The Calvin cycle?
Glucose			
O_2			
CO_2			
H_2O			
ATP			
ADP + P_i			
NADPH			
NADP$^+$			

4. Which light reaction system (cyclic or noncyclic) would a chloroplast use in each situation?

a. Plenty of light is available, but the cell contains little NADP$^+$.	b. There is plenty of light, and the cell contains a high concentration of NADP$^+$.

5. All living organisms require a constant supply of ATP to maintain life. If no light is available, how can a plant make ATP?

Extend Your
Understanding **Activity 10.2 Chloroplast Function under Different Conditions**

Chloroplast thylakoids can be isolated and purified for biochemical experiments. Shown below is an experiment in which pH was measured in a suspension of isolated thylakoids before and after light illumination (first arrow). At the time indicated by the second arrow, a chemical compound was added to the thylakoids. Examine these data and address the following questions.

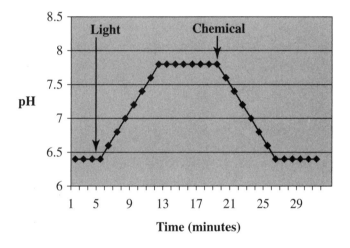

a. Based on your understanding of the function of the chloroplasts, why does turning on the light cause the pH in the solution outside the thylakoids to increase?

b. Given the response, the chemical added was probably an inhibitor of:
   (A) oxidative phosphorylation
   (B) ATP synthase
   (C) NADPH breakdown
   (D) electron transport chain between photosystems I and II
   (E) RUBISCO

Justify your answer

Name ————————————— Course/Section —————————————

Date ————————————— Professor/TA —————————————

 Activity 10.3 How do C$_3$, C$_4$, and CAM photosynthesis compare?

1. Carbon dioxide enters plant leaves through the stomata, while oxygen (the photosynthetic waste product) and water from the leaves exit through the stomata. Plants must constantly balance both water loss and energy gain (as photosynthesis). This has led to the evolution of various modifications of C$_3$ photosynthesis.

	C$_3$	C$_4$	CAM
Draw simplified diagrams of the cross sections of a leaf from a C$_3$, a C$_4$, and a CAM plant.			
a. How are the leaves similar?			
b. How are the leaves different?			
c. How and when does carbon dioxide get into each leaf?			
d. Which enzyme(s) (1) capture carbon dioxide and (2) carry it to the Calvin cycle?	(1) (2)	(1) (2)	(1) (2)

e. What makes C$_4$ photosynthesis more efficient than C$_3$ photosynthesis in tropical climates?

f. How is CAM photosynthesis advantageous in desert climates?

2. Photosynthesis evolved very early in Earth's history. Central to the evolution of photosynthesis was the evolution of the enzyme rubisco (an abbreviation for ribulose bisphosphate carboxylase oxidase). To the best of our knowledge, all photosynthetic plants use rubisco. Rubisco's function is to supply carbon dioxide to the Calvin cycle; however, it does this only if the ratio of carbon dioxide to oxygen is relatively high. (For comparison, a relatively high ratio of carbon dioxide to oxygen is 0.03% carbon dioxide to 20% oxygen.) When the ratio of carbon dioxide to oxygen becomes low, the role of rubisco switches and it catalyzes photorespiration, the breakdown of glucose to carbon dioxide and water.

a. Why could we call photorespiration a "mistake" in the functioning of the cell?

b. Rubisco is thought to have evolved when Earth had a reducing atmosphere. How does that hypothesis help explain this "mistake"?

Name ——————————— Course/Section ————————————

Date ——————————— Professor/TA ————————————

Activity 11.1 What is mitosis?

What is mitosis?

1. What is the overall purpose of mitosis?

2. In what types of organism(s) and cells does mitosis occur? What type of cell division occurs in bacteria?

What are the stages of mitosis?

3. The fruit fly, *Drosophila melanogaster*, has a total of eight chromosomes (four pairs) in each of its somatic cells. Somatic cells are all cells of the body except those that will divide to form the gametes (ova or sperm). Review the events that occur in the various stages of mitosis.

Keep in mind that the stages of cell division were first recognized from an examination of fixed slides of tissues undergoing division. On fixed slides, cells are captured or frozen at particular points in the division cycle. Using these static slides, early microscopists identified specific arrangements or patterns of chromosomes that occurred at various stages of the cycle and gave these stages names (interphase, prophase, and so on). Later work using time-lapse photography made it clear that mitosis is a continuous process. Once division begins, the chromosomes move fluidly from one phase to the next.

Assume you are a microscopist viewing fruit-fly cells that are undergoing mitosis. In each of the circles (cell membranes) on the following page, draw what you would expect to see if you were looking at a cell in the stage of mitosis indicated. If no circle is present, draw what you would expect to see at the given stage.

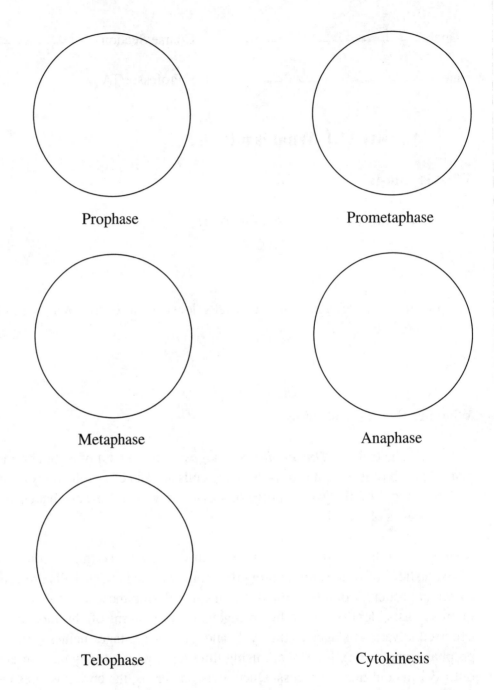

Prophase

Prometaphase

Metaphase

Anaphase

Telophase

Cytokinesis

Daughter cells in interphase

What are the products of mitosis?

4. How many cells are produced at the end of a single mitotic division?

5. How many different kinds of cells are produced at the end of a single mitotic division?

6. Six centromeres are observed in a prophase cell from another species of insect.

a. How many pairs of chromosomes does this organism contain?		
b. For each stage of mitosis, indicate the number of centromeres you would expect to find and the number of copies of chromosomes attached to each centromere.		
Stage of mitosis:	Number of centromeres visible per cell	Number of chromosome copies attached to each centromere
Prophase		
Anaphase		

What controls mitosis?

7. Checkpoints in the normal cell cycle prevent cells from going through division if problems occur—for example, if the DNA is damaged.

    a. What forms do the checkpoints take? That is, how do they control whether or not cell division occurs?

b. On this page, develop a handout or diagram to explain how these checkpoints work under normal conditions. Your handout should include a description of each checkpoint, where it acts in the cell cycle, and what each checkpoint does to control cell division.

c. Cancer results from uncontrolled cell division. Explain how mutations in one or more of the checkpoints might lead to cancer.

Activity 12.1 What is meiosis?

What is meiosis?

1. What is the overall purpose of meiosis?

2. In what types of organism(s) does meiosis occur? What type of cell division occurs in bacteria?

What are the stages of meiosis?

3. The fruit fly, *Drosophila melanogaster*, has a total of eight chromosomes (four pairs) in each of its somatic cells. Somatic cells are all cells of the body except those that will divide to form the gametes (ova or sperm). Review the events that occur in the various stages of meiosis.

Keep in mind that the stages of cell division were first recognized from an examination of fixed slides of tissues undergoing division. On fixed slides, cells are captured or frozen at particular points in the division cycle. Using these static slides, early microscopists identified specific arrangements or patterns of chromosomes that occurred at various stages of the cycle and gave these stages names (interphase, prophase I, and so on). Later work using time-lapse photography made it clear that meiosis is a continuous process. Once division begins, the chromosomes move fluidly from one phase to the next.

Assume you are a microscopist viewing fruit-fly cells that are undergoing meiosis. In each of the circles (cell membranes) on the following pages, draw what you would expect to see if you were looking at a cell in the stage of meiosis indicated. If no circle is present, draw what you would expect to see at the given stage.

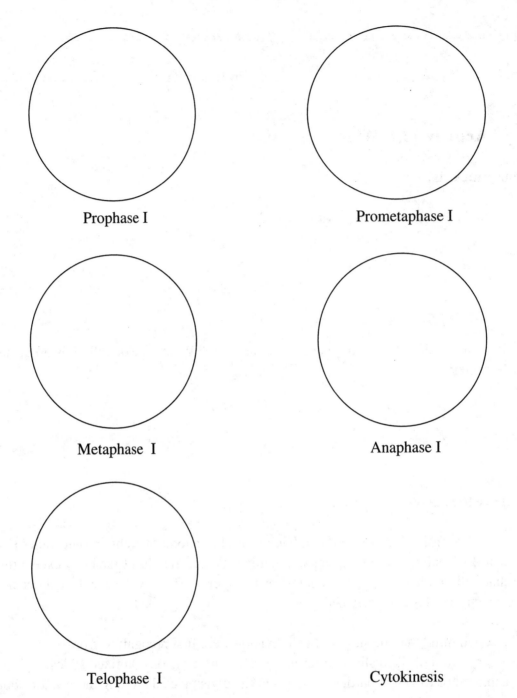

Prophase I

Prometaphase I

Metaphase I

Anaphase I

Telophase I

Cytokinesis

Daughter Cells

Follow one daughter cell through meiosis II.

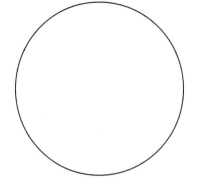

Prophase II

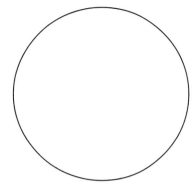

Prometaphase II

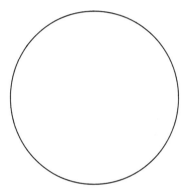

Metaphase II

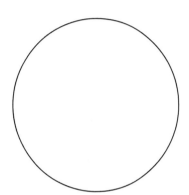

Anaphase II

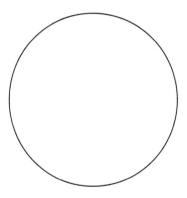

Telophase II

Cytokinesis

Daughter Cells

What are the products of meiosis?

4. Consider a single cell going through meiosis.

   a. How many cells are produced at the end of meiosis?

   b. How many chromosomes, and which chromosomes, does each of the daughter cells contain?

5. Six centromeres are observed in a prophase I cell from another species of insect.

a. How many pairs of chromosomes does this organism contain?		
b. For each stage of meiosis, indicate the number of centromeres you would expect to find and the number of copies of chromosomes attached to each centromere.		
Stage of meiosis:	Number of centromeres visible per cell	Number of chromosome copies attached to each centromere
Anaphase I		
Prophase II		

Name ———————————— Course/Section ————————————

Date ———————————— Professor/TA ————————————

Extend Your
Understanding **Activity 12.2 Sex Chromosome Trisomy due**
to Nondisjunction

1 to 4. Nondisjunction of sex chromosomes during human gamete formation may lead to individuals with sex chromosome trisomy. An individual with the sex chromosome trisomy of XXY may have resulted from nondisjunction occurring in:

T/F   1.   meiosis I in the father's sperm production

T/F   2.   meiosis II in the father's sperm production

T/F   3.   meiosis I in the mother's egg production

T/F   4.   meiosis II in the mother's egg production

Name ——————————————— Course/Section ———————————————

Date ——————————————— Professor/TA ———————————————

Extend Your
Understanding **Activity 12.3 An Experiment Designed to Test
the "Changing-Environment Hypothesis"**

You are employed as a consultant at a large paper company, because the company is concerned about defoliation caused by insects in its poplar plantations. Insect damage can have severe effects on tree health, and can even cause tree mortality in large areas of forest. The paper company is considering altering the way it grows trees from a one-species plantation to more of a natural multispecies forest setting, in response to the insect damage. After consulting with a forest entomologist, you find out that the insect most prevalent in the poplar plantations is the poplar tentmaker (*Icthyura inclusa*), but you also find the cottonwood leaf beetle (*Chrysomela scripta*) present. Most trees can reproduce both vegetatively (asexual clones) and sexually; poplar trees are known to produce huge tracts of clonal shoots, and a single tree can produce hundreds of thousands of seeds per year.

Given that there can be both sexual and asexual reproduction in poplar trees, you decide that it would be a good idea to test the changing-environment hypothesis for this site, in comparison to a nearby natural forest that has a mixture of poplar, red oak, and black cherry. You collect data at ten 10-m^2 plots at each site (plantation and forest) based on two factors: percentage of infected trees and percentage of trees that are clonal versus sexually reproduced. The data you collect are provided in the chart below.

a. Fill in the missing values in the data table, and draw a graph that best describes the mean and variability of the data. The formula for standard error = standard deviation/square root of the number of samples.

	Plantation site		Forest site	
	Percent infected trees	Percent clonal	Percent infected trees	Percent clonal
Plot 1	22	84	24	45
Plot 2	19	81	23	52
Plot 3	26	76	28	55
Plot 4	24	74	17	47
Plot 5	28	82	25	56
Plot 6	18	83	16	43
Plot 7	22	79	21	49
Plot 8	25	73	26	52
Plot 9	23	86	19	51

(Continued)

	Plantation site		Forest site	
	Percent infected trees	Percent clonal	Percent infected trees	Percent clonal
Plot 10	19	84	22	48
Mean	22.6			
SD (Standard Deviation)	3.27	4.52	3.90	4.18
N (Number of samples)	10			
SE (Standard Error)	1.03			

b. What do the results from the table and graph mean? Do they support or refute the changing-environment hypothesis? What would you recommend to the paper company?

c. Propose an alternate hypothesis to explain the results in your graph.

Name _____   Course/Section _____

Date _____   Professor/TA _____

 Integrate Your Understanding **Chapters 11–12—How do mitosis and meiosis differ?**

Review the processes of mitosis and meiosis in Chapters 11 and 12 of *Biological Science*, 4th edition, and then fill in the following chart.

1. What events occur during each phase of mitosis and meiosis?

	Interphase	Prophase	Metaphase	Anaphase	Telophase & cytokinesis
Mitosis	For example: G_1—cell growth S—DNA duplication G_2—cell growth		For example: Duplicated chromosomes, each with two sister chromatids, line up independently on the metaphase plate.		
Meiosis I					
Meiosis II					

2. Fill in this chart to summarize the major similarities and differences in the two types of cell division (mitosis vs. meiosis). For similarities, include the event(s) that always happen(s) in prophase, for example, no matter which of the cell division cycles you're describing.

	Interphase	Prophase	Metaphase	Anaphase	Telophase
a. What similarities do you see?					
b. What differences do you see?					

c. If the amount of DNA in a somatic cell equals C during G_1 of interphase, **then** how much DNA is present in the cell during each phase of mitosis **and meiosis**?					
Amount of DNA in:	Interphase	Prophase	Metaphase	Anaphase	Telophase
Mitosis					
Meiosis I					
Meiosis II					

d. How do the similarities in prophase of mitosis and meiosis compare with the similarities in telophase of mitosis and meiosis?

e. At what stage(s) does/do most of the differences among mitosis, meiosis I, and meiosis II occur? Why do these differences exist?

Name_____   Course/Section_____

Date_____   Professor/TA_____

 Activity 13.1 A Genetics Vocabulary Review

Mendel did not know anything about chromosomes, genes, or DNA. Because modern genetics uses vocabulary that assumes students today understand these ideas, however, it's helpful to review some key terms.

Match each commonly used genetics term with its appropriate definition or example.

Terms	**Definitions and Examples**
___ heterozygous	a. Blue-eyed blonde mates with brown-eyed brunette
___ homozygous	b. *BB* or *bb*
___ monohybrid cross	c. not on sex chromosomes
___ autosomal	d. blue or brown eyes
___ genotype	e. *Bb*
___ phenotype	f. locus on a chromosome that codes for a given polypeptide*
___ gene	g. Blonde mates with brunette.
___ allele	h. *BB*, *Bb*, or *bb*
___ dihybrid cross	i. Males have only one for each gene on the X chromosome

Note: It is true that a gene can code for a polypeptide. However, not all genes code for polypeptides. Some code for mRNAs that produce polypeptides, but others code for other forms of RNA—for example, rRNA and tRNA.

Name _____   Course/Section _____

Date _____   Professor/TA _____

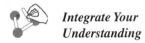

Integrate Your
Understanding **Chapters 12–13—Modeling Meiosis: How can diploid organisms produce haploid gametes?**

Integrate your understanding of meiosis (Chapter 12) and of basic Mendelian principles (Chapter 13) to develop a dynamic model of meiosis. When you've completed the model, use it to explain what aspects of meiosis account for Mendel's laws of segregation and independent assortment.

Building the Model

Working in groups of three or four, construct a dynamic (claymation-type) model of meiosis for the organism described on the next page. You may use the materials provided in class or devise your own.

When developing and explaining your model, be sure to include definitions or descriptions of all these terms and structures:

diploid	dominant allele
$2n/n$	genotype
chromosome	maternal
chromatid	paternal
chromatin	spindle
centromere (kinetochore)	spindle fibers
autosome	nuclear membrane
sex chromosome	nucleolus
sex cell	phenotype
autosome	heterozygous
crossing over	homozygous
synapsis	law of segregation
recessive allele	law of independent assortment

What genetic and chromosomal traits does your organism have?

1. Your individual is male/female (choose one). Females are XX and males are XY. For simplicity, assume that the individual is diploid with $2n = 6$, including the sex chromosomes. On one pair of autosomes (the nonsex chromosomes), the individual is heterozygous for hair color (B = brown and dominant, b = blonde and recessive). On another pair of autosomes, the organism is heterozygous for hair structure (C = curly and dominant, c = straight and recessive). Assume further that the individual's mother was homozygous dominant for both traits, and the father was homozygous recessive for both.

   a. Is your individual's hair curly or straight? Brown or blonde?

   b. What did the individual's mother's hair look like? What did the father's hair look like?

   c. What chromosomes and alleles were in the egg and the sperm that gave rise to your individual?

What does the nucleus contain?

First develop a model of a cell from your individual.

- Use chalk on a tabletop, or a marker on a large sheet of paper, to draw a cell's membrane and its nuclear membrane. The nucleus should be at least 9 inches in diameter.
- Use playdough or cut out pieces of paper to represent your individual's chromosomes. Indicate the placement of genes on the chromosomes. Put all the chromosomes from your individual into the nucleus.
- Make a key for your model that indicates how alleles are designated and which of the chromosomes are maternal versus paternal contributions.

Then develop a model of the meiotically active cell.

- Make an identical copy of the original cell. This will be the "active" cell—that is, the one that undergoes meiosis.
- Using the "active" cell only, develop a dynamic model of meiosis. To do this, actively move the chromosomes of this one cell through a complete round of

Integrate Your Understanding Chapters 12–13

meiosis in a sex cell. (Sex cells are the cells of the body that give rise to gametes: ova or sperm.)

- Use your model to demonstrate meiosis to another student group or to your instructor. Then use your model to answer the questions on the next page.

What are the products of meiosis?

2. From a single sex cell going through meiosis, how many daughter cells are produced?

3. How many different kinds of gametes are produced from a single cell undergoing meiosis? (Assume no crossing over occurs.)

4. Your individual is heterozygous for two genes on separate pairs of homologous chromosomes. His or her genotype is *CcBb*. Given this information alone, how many different kinds of gametes could this individual produce? (Again assume no crossing over occurs.)

5. Compare your answer to question 4 with your answer to question 3. How do the numbers of different gametes in your answers compare? Explain any difference.

6. What aspect(s) of meiosis account(s) for Mendel's laws of:

a. Segregation?

b. Independent assortment?

Activity 13.2 A Quick Guide to Solving Genetics Problems

Over the years, rules have been developed for setting up genetics problems and denoting genes and their alleles in these problems. This activity provides a quick review of some of these rules. After you have read through all of this material, complete Activities 13.3, 13.4, and 13.5.

Basic Assumptions to Make When Solving Genetics Problems

1. Are the genes linked?
If the problem does not (a) indicate that the genes are linked or (b) ask whether the genes are (or could be) linked, then you should assume that the genes are not linked.

2. Are the genes sex-linked?
Similarly, if the problem does not (a) indicate that the genes are sex-linked (that is, on the X chromosome) or (b) ask whether the genes are (or could be) on the X chromosome (or Y chromosome), then you should assume that the genes are on autosomes and are not sex-linked.

3. Is there a lethal allele?
If a gene is lethal, then you should assume that the offspring that get the lethal allele (if dominant) or alleles (if homozygous recessive) do not appear; that is, they are not born, do not hatch, and so on. Therefore, they are not counted among the offspring. (An obvious exception is lethal genes that have their effect late in life. If this is the case, however, it should be noted in the question.)

4. Are the alleles dominant, recessive, or neither?
Unless the problem states otherwise, assume that capital letters (*BB*, for example) designate dominant alleles and lowercase letters (*bb*, for example) indicate recessive alleles. When there is codominance or incomplete dominance, the alleles are usually designated by the same capital letter and each one is given a superscript (for example, $I^A I^B$ in Figure 13.18, page 247 of *Biological Science*, 4th edition).

5. How are genotypes written?
Assume a gene for fur color in hamsters is located on the number 1 pair of homologous autosomes. Brown fur (*B*) is dominant over white fur (*b*). The genotype for fur color can be designated in different ways:

a. The alleles can be shown associated with the number 1 chromosome. In this notation, an individual heterozygous for this gene is designated as $|^B|^b$.

b. Most commonly, this notation is simplified to *Bb*.

In problems that involve sex-linked genes, the chromosomes are always indicated—for example, X^AX^a and X^aY.

6. What information do you need to gather before trying to solve a genetics problem?

Before trying to solve any problem, answer these questions:

a. What information is provided? For example, what type of cross is it? Is it a monohybrid or dihybrid cross? Are the genes sex-linked or autosomal? Linked or unlinked?

b. What does the information provided tell you about the gene(s) in question? For example:
   - What phenotypes can result?
   - How many alleles does the gene have?
   - Are the alleles of the gene dominant? Recessive? Codominant?

c. Does the question supply any information about the individuals' genotypes? If so, what information is provided?
   - Grandparent information?
   - Parental (P) information?
   - Gamete possibilities?
   - Offspring possibilities?

Solving Genetics Problems

1. What is a Punnett square?

Punnett squares are frequently used in solving genetics problems. A Punnett square is a device that allows you to determine all the possible paired combinations of two sets of characteristics. For example, if you wanted to determine all the possible combinations of red, blue, and green shirts with red, blue, and green pants, you could set up this Punnett square:

		Shirts		
		Red shirt	Blue shirt	Green shirt
Pants	Red pants			
	Blue pants			
	Green pants			

Similarly, if you wanted to determine the probability of a male (XY) and a female (XX) having a son or a daughter, you would first determine the possible gametes each could produce and then set up a Punnett square to look at all the possible combinations of male and female gametes. Here meiosis dictates that the female gametes get one of her X chromosomes or the other. In the male, the gametes get either the X chromosome or the Y. As a result, the Punnett square would look like this:

		Female's gamete possibilities	
		X	X
Male's gamete possibilities	X	XX	XX
	Y	XY	XY

2. **If you know the parents' genotypes, how can you determine what types of offspring they will produce?**

   a. **Autosomal genes:** For an autosomal gene that has the alleles A and a, there are three possible genotypes: AA, Aa, and aa.

   All possible combinations of matings and offspring for two individuals carrying the autosomal gene with alleles A and a are shown in the figure below.

   If you know how to solve these six crosses, you can solve any problem involving one or more autosomal genes.

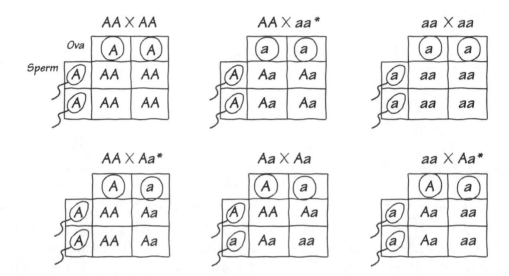

Note: If you take sex into account, there are actually nine possible combinations of matings:

Male genotypes	Female genotypes		
	AA	Aa	aa
AA	$AA \times AA$	$AA \times Aa$	$AA \times aa$
Aa	$Aa \times AA$	$Aa \times Aa$	$Aa \times aa$
aa	$AA \times aa$	$aa \times Aa$	$aa \times aa$

Because the results of reciprocal autosomal matings (e.g., AA male with aa female and aa male with AA female) are the same, those matings are highlighted in the nine combinations above.

b. **Sex-linked genes:** For sex-linked genes, females have three possible genotypes: $X^{w+}X^{w+}$, $X^{w+}X^w$, and X^wX^w. Males have only two possible genotypes: $X^{w+}Y$ and X^wY. All the possible combinations of matings and offspring for a sex-linked trait are listed in the next figure. If you know how to solve these six single-gene crosses, then you can solve any genetics problem involving sex-linked genes.

All possible combinations of matings and offspring for two individuals with a sex-linked gene are shown in the figure below.

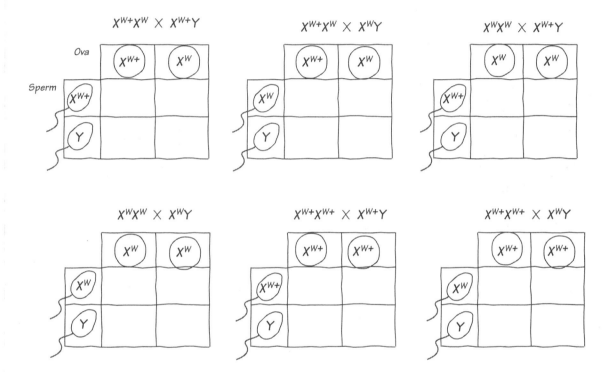

c. **Multiple genes:** Remember, if genes are on separate chromosomes, then they assort independently in meiosis. Therefore, to solve a genetics problem involving multiple genes, where each gene is on a separate pair of homologous chromosomes:
   - Solve for each gene separately.
   - Determine probabilities for combination (multiple-gene) genotypes by multiplying the probabilities of the individual genotypes.

Example:

What is the probability that two individuals of the genotype *AaBb* and *aaBb* will have any *aabb* offspring?

To answer this, solve for each gene separately.
A cross of *Aa* × *aa* could produce the following offspring:

	A	a
a	Aa	aa
a	Aa	aa

½ *Aa* and ½ *aa* offspring

A cross of *Bb* × *Bb* could produce the following offspring:

	B	b
B	BB	Bb
b	Bb	bb

¼ *BB*, ½ *Bb* and ¼ *bb* offspring

The probability of having any *aabb* offspring is then the probability of having any *aa* offspring multiplied by the probability of having any *bb* offspring.

The probability is ½ × ¼ = ⅛

Name ______________________ Course/Section ______________________

Date ______________________ Professor/TA ______________________

Activity 13.3 How can you determine all the possible types of gametes?

To solve genetics problems in which genotypes are given, you must first know what types of gametes each organism can produce.

1. How many different kinds of gametes can individuals with each of the following genotypes produce?

   a. *AA*

   b. *aa*

   c. *Aa*

   d. *AaBB*

   e. *AaBb*

   f. *AaBbCC*

   g. *AaBbCc*

   h. *AaBbCcDdEeFf*

2. Based on your answer in question 1, propose a general rule for determining the number of different gametes organisms like those described in question 1 can produce.

3. Two individuals have the genotypes *AaBbCcDd*.

   a. How many different types of gametes can each produce?

   b. What are these gametes?

   c. You set up a Punnett square using all the possible gametes for both individuals. How many "offspring squares" are in this Punnett square?

   d. If you completed this Punnett square, how easy would it be to find all the "offspring squares" that contain the genotype *AaBBccDd*?

   e. Given that the genes are all on separate pairs of homologous chromosomes, what other method(s) could you use to determine the probability of these individuals having any offspring with the genotype *AaBbccDd*?

Activity 13.4 Solving Problems When the Genetics Are Known

Refer to Activity 13.3 and to Chapter 13 in *Biological Science*, 4th edition, to complete this activity.

1. An organism that has the genotype *AaBbCc* is crossed with an organism that has the genotype *AABbCc*. Assume all genes are on separate sets of chromosomes (that is, they are not linked).

   a. What is the probability that any of the offspring will have the genotype *AABBCC*? (*Hint:* To get the answer, consider the six possible types of autosomal crosses. Determine the individual probabilities of getting *AA* offspring from the monohybrid cross. Then do the same to determine the probabilities of getting *BB* offspring and *CC* offspring. Multiply these probabilities together.)

   b. What is the probability that any of the offspring will have the genotype *AaBbcc*?

2. Consider the cross *AaBbCcddEe* × *AABBccDDEe*.

   a. What is the probability that any offspring will have the genotype *AaBBCcDdEE*?

   b. What is the probability that any offspring will have the genotype *AABBCCDDee*?

3. In cattle, primarily Holsteins, there is an X-linked disease that causes hairlessness with tooth problems; the disease is called anhidrotic ectodermal dysplasia (AED). Affected cattle have little hair, few sweat glands, and no incisors.

   a. What is the probability that a heterozygous female Holstein mated with an affected male will produce any affected (AED) offspring?
   $X^{a+} X^a \times X^a Y$ = heterozygous female crossed with an AED male (a^+ = unaffected; a = affected)

b. What is the probability that the mating in part a will produce any affected females?

c. What is the probability that this mating will produce any diseased males?

4. A heterozygous brown-eyed human female who is a carrier of color blindness marries a blue-eyed male who is not color-blind. Color blindness is a sex-linked trait. Assume that eye color is an autosomal trait and that brown is dominant over blue. What is the probability that any of the offspring produced have the traits listed?

a. brown eyes

b. blue eyes

c. color blindness

d. color-blind males

e. brown-eyed, color-blind males

f. blue-eyed, color-blind females

g. What is the probability that any of the males will be color blind?

h. Why do males show sex-linked traits more often than females?

Name _____   Course/Section _____

Date _____   Professor/TA _____

Activity 13.5 Solving Problems When the Genetics Are Unknown

An understanding of Mendelian genetics allows us to determine the theoretical probabilities associated with normal transmission of autosomal and sex-linked alleles during reproduction. This understanding provides us with strategies for solving genetics problems. In real-life situations, geneticists use these strategies to determine the genetics behind specific phenotypic traits in organisms. They do this by conducting controlled crosses of experimental organisms (e.g., *Drosophila*) or by analyzing family pedigrees (e.g., humans).

Part One: Controlled crosses

Two problems are presented below. In each, you are given:

(a) "Wild population"—the phenotypic characteristics of a wild population of fruit flies that were trapped randomly on a remote island.

(b) "Cross 1, 2, etc."—the phenotypic characteristics of offspring from a controlled cross. The phenotypes of the parents are indicated after each cross (e.g., "Cross 1: Male Ambler X Female Wild Type").

For each of the problems, analyze the results in each cross and answer the questions that follow.

Problem 1

Wild population	Wild type	Ambler	Total
Male	33	17	50
Female	31	19	50
Total	64	36	100

Cross 1: Male Ambler × Female Wild Type

Offspring Vial 1	Wild type	Ambler	Total
Male	29	24	53
Female	29	31	50
Total	58	55	113

a. What does cross 1 tell you about dominance versus recessiveness of the alleles?

b. What does cross 1 tell you about placement of the alleles on autosomes versus sex chromosomes? (If you can determine this, your answer must show the chromosomal genotypes for the parents in this cross.)

Cross 2: Female Ambler × Male Wild Type

Offspring Vial 2	Wild type	Ambler	Total
Male	0	32	32
Female	32	0	32
Total	32	32	64

a. What does cross 2 tell you about dominance versus recessiveness of the alleles?

b. What does cross 2 tell you about placement of the alleles on autosomes versus sex chromosomes? (In your answer, show the chromosomal genotypes for the parents in this cross.)

Problem 2

Mt = Monocle; Bt = Bifocal; Tr = Trifocal; Sp = Spinner; Sh = Shiny

Wild Population	Mt, Sp	Mt, Sh	Bt, Sp	Bt, Sh	Tr, Sp	Tr, Sh	Total
Male	10	6	6	0	22	3	46
Female	19	1	9	1	20	4	54
Total	29	6	15	1	42	7	100

Cross 1: Bifocal, Spinner Female × Monocle, Shiny Male

Mt = Monocle; *Bt* = Bifocal; *TR* = Trifocal; *Sp* = Spinner; *Sh* = Shiny

Offspring Vial 1	*Mt, Sp*	*Mt, Sh*	*Bt, Sp*	*Bt, Sh*	*Tr, Sp*	*Tr, Sh*	Total
Male	0	0	0	0	31	34	65
Female	0	0	0	0	34	38	72
Total	0	0	0	0	65	72	137

a. What does cross 1 tell you about dominance versus recessiveness of the alleles?

b. What does cross 1 tell you about placement of the alleles on autosomes versus sex chromosomes?

Cross 2: Monocle, Spinner Female × Trifocal, Spinner Male

Mt = Monocle; *Bt* = Bifocal; *Tr* = Trifocal; *Sp* = Spinner; *Sh* = Shiny

Offspring Vial 2	*Mt, Sp*	*Mt, Sh*	*Bt, Sp*	*Bt, Sh*	*Tr, Sp*	*Tr, Sh*	Total
Male	8	8	0	0	8	8	32
Female	23	0	0	0	15	0	38
Total	31	8	0	0	23	8	70

a. What does cross 2 tell you about dominance versus recessiveness of the alleles?

b. What does cross 2 tell you about placement of the alleles on autosomes vs. sex chromosomes?

Part Two: Analysis of pedigrees

Analyze the pedigree and answer the questions that follow.

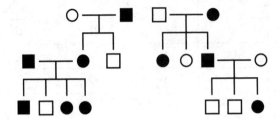

The diagram above shows a pedigree of three generations in a family. Filled circles and squares indicate persons with a genetic disorder. A square indicates a male, and a circle indicates a female. The 2 males in generation 1 are siblings, in this case, brothers.

1. Looking only at the generation 2 offspring (of the two generation 1 brothers), what can you say about the gene(s) controlling the genetic disorder? For example, is the disorder caused by a gene that is dominant, recessive, autosomal, sex-linked?

2. What additional information do you gain from examining the generation 3 offspring?

Name _____   Course/Section _____

Date _____   Professor/TA _____

 Activity 13.6 How can the mode of inheritance be determined experimentally?

Outline the experimental crosses you would need to make to solve each problem.

1. Three new traits have been discovered in a population of *Drosophila:*

    • Tapping (a behavioral mutant in which the fly taps one foot constantly)
    • Single stripe (a pigmentation change that leads to a long stripe down the fly's back)
    • Angular (causes angular bends in bristles that are normally straight)

    The positions of the three genes on the chromosomes are unknown. Given two pure-breeding (homozygous) lines and using an initial cross of normal, normal, normal females with tapping, single stripe, angular males, describe the appropriate genetic experiments needed to establish whether any of these traits are caused by genes that are:

    a. Autosomal or sex-linked

    b. Linked on the same chromosome or unlinked

2. A genetics student chose a special project involving a three-gene cross to check the relative positions and map distances separating three genes in *Drosophila* that she thought were all on the third chromosome. To do this, she mated *Drosophila* females that were homozygous for the recessive genes *cu* (curled), *sr* (striped), and *e* (ebony) with males that were homozygous for the wild type, cu^+ (straight), sr^+ (not striped), and e^+ (gray). She then mated (testcrossed) the F_1 females with homozygous recessive curled, striped, ebony males.

Here are the phenotypic results of the testcross:

straight, gray, not striped	820
curled, ebony, striped	810
straight, ebony, striped	100
curled, gray, not striped	97
straight, ebony, not striped	80
curled, gray, striped	90
straight, gray, striped	1
curled, ebony, not striped	2
Total:	2000

a. How are the three genes arranged on the chromosomes?

b. What evidence allows you to answer the question in part a?

c. If any of the genes are linked, how far apart are they on the chromosome? How can you determine this?

Name —————————————   Course/Section ————————————

Date —————————————   Professor/TA ————————————

 Activity 14.1 Is the hereditary material DNA or protein?

Accumulating and Analyzing the Evidence

Build a concept map to review the evidence used to determine that DNA was the genetic material, the structure of DNA, and its mode of replication. Recall from Activity 4.1 and Chapter 4 in *Biological Science*, 4th edition, how Watson and Crick determined the structure of DNA. Keep in mind that there are many ways to construct a concept map.

- First, develop a separate concept map for each set of terms (A to D on the next page). Begin by writing each term on a separate Post-it note or sheet of paper.
- Then organize each set of terms into a map that indicates how the terms are associated or related.
- Draw lines between the terms, and add action phrases to the lines to indicate how the terms are related.

Here is an example:

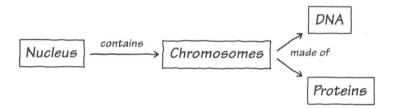

- After you have completed each of the individual concept maps, merge or interrelate the maps to show the overall logic used to conclude that DNA (not protein) is the heredity material.
- When you have completed the overall concept map, answer the questions.

TERMS:

Map A

Griffith

mice

S strain of *Streptococcus*

R strain of *Streptococcus*

live

heat-killed

transformation

Avery, McCarty, and MacLeod

DNA

protein

Map B

Hershey and Chase

bacteria

bacteriophage (phage) (only a protein and DNA)

^{35}S

^{32}P

Waring blender

high-velocity centrifugation

Map C

Watson and Crick

X-ray crystallography

Chargaff's rule

purine structure

pyrimidine structure

H bonds

phosphate sugar backbone

Map D

Meselson and Stahl

conservative

dispersive

semiconservative

nucleic acid bases

^{14}N

^{15}N

bacteria

density equilibrium centrifugation

replication

1. In the early to mid-1900s, there was considerable debate about whether protein or DNA was the hereditary material.

   a. For what reasons did many researchers assume that protein was the genetic material?

b. What key sets of experiments led to the understanding that, in fact, DNA and not protein was the hereditary material?	c. What evidence did each experiment provide?
Griffith experimented with a lethal S strain of bacteria and a nonlethal R strain of the same bacterial species. S strain injected into mice killed them. R strain didn't, and neither did heat-killed S strain. If heat-killed S and live R strains were mixed and injected simultaneously, however, the mice died. When autopsied, live S bacteria were found.	

2. Watson and Crick were the first to correctly describe the structure of DNA. What evidence did they use to do this? How did they use this evidence to put together or propose the structure of DNA?

3. How did the results of Meselson and Stahl's experiments show that DNA replicates semiconservatively? To respond to this, answer the following questions.

   a. Diagram the results that would be expected for each type of replication proposed.

   b. What evidence allowed Meselson and Stahl to eliminate the conservative model?

   c. What evidence allowed them to eliminate the dispersive model?

Extend Your
Understanding **Activity 14.2 How do bacteria replicate their DNA?**

An *E. coli* cell that contains a single circular chromosome made of double-stranded DNA is allowed to replicate for many generations in an ^{15}N medium until all of the *E. coli* cells' DNA is labeled with ^{15}N (nitrogen 15). One *E. coli* cell is removed from the ^{15}N medium and is placed into medium in which all of the available nucleotides are ^{14}N labeled. The *E. coli* cell is allowed to replicate until 8 *E. coli* are formed.

1. Given this scenario, which of the following statements is true?

    a. Some ^{15}N-labeled DNA will be found in all eight cells.

    b. Some ^{15}N-labeled DNA will be found in only four of the cells.

    c. Some ^{15}N-labeled DNA will be found in only two of the cells.

    d. Some ^{15}N-labeled DNA will be found in only one of the cells.

2. Draw the sequence of events that occurred to explain your answer.

Name ——————————————   Course/Section ——————————————

Date ——————————————   Professor/TA ——————————————

 Activity 14.3 How does DNA replicate?

Working in groups of three or four, construct a dynamic (working or active) model of DNA replication. You may use the materials provided in class or devise your own.

Building the Model

- Develop a model of a short segment of double-stranded DNA.
- Include a key for your model that indicates what each component represents in the DNA molecule—for example, adenine, phosphate group, deoxyribose.
- Create a dynamic (claymation-type) model of replication. Actively move the required bases, enzymes, and other components needed to model replication of your DNA segment.

Your model should describe the roles and relationships of all the following enzymes and structures in replication:

parental DNA	$3' \to 5'$ versus $5' \to 3'$
nucleotide excision repair	nitrogenous bases A, T, G, C
daughter DNA	replication fork
mutation	replication bubble
antiparallel strands	Okazaki fragment
single-stranded DNA-binding proteins	DNA polymerase
leading strand	helicase
telomeres	DNA ligase
lagging strand	primase
telomerase	RNA primers
5' end	origin of replication
3' end	

Use your model to answer these questions.

1. How did Meselson and Stahl's experiments support the idea that DNA replication is semiconservative?

2. A new form of DNA is discovered that appears to be able to replicate itself both in the $3' \rightarrow 5'$ direction and in the $5' \rightarrow 3'$ direction. If this is true, how would this newly discovered DNA replication differ from DNA replication as we know it?

3. Amazingly, an alien species of cellular organism is found alive in the remains of a meteorite that landed in the Mojave Desert. As a scientist, you are trying to determine whether this alien life-form uses DNA, protein, or some other type of compound as its hereditary material.

    a. What kinds of experiments would you propose to determine what the hereditary material is?

    b. If the hereditary material turns out to be similar to our DNA, describe the simplest experiments you could run to try to determine if it is double-stranded like our DNA, triple-stranded, or what.

4. Some researchers estimate that the mutation rate for any given gene (or its DNA) in certain strains of bacteria is about 10^{-8}. This means that one error or mutation in a given gene is introduced for every 100 million cell divisions.

    a. What can cause mistakes in replication?

    b. How are such mistakes normally corrected?

Name ————————————   Course/Section ————————————

Date ————————————   Professor/TA ————————————

Integrate Your
Understanding **Chapters 15–16—Modeling Transcription and Translation: What processes produce RNA from DNA and protein from mRNA?**

Create a model of the processes of transcription and translation. Your model should be a dynamic (working or active) representation of the events that occur first in transcription in the nucleus and then in translation in the cytoplasm.

When developing and explaining your model, be sure to include definitions or descriptions of the following terms and structures:

gene

DNA

nucleotides: A, T, G, and C versus A, U, G, and C

RNA modification(s) after transcription

mRNA

RNA polymerase

poly(A) tail

5′ cap

translation

protein synthesis

ribosome (large versus small subunit)

A, P, and E sites

tRNA

rRNA

start codon (methionine)

aminoacyl-tRNA synthetase

amino acids (see Figure 15.6 on page 284 in *Biological Science*, 4th edition)

peptidyl transferase

polypeptide

energy

codons

stop codons

anticodons

initiation

elongation

termination

polypeptide

For the purposes of this activity, assume there are *no introns* in the mRNA transcript.

Building the Model

- Use chalk on a tabletop, or a marker on a large sheet of paper, to draw a cell's plasma membrane and nuclear membrane. The nucleus should have a diameter of about 12 inches.
- Draw a DNA molecule in the nucleus that contains the following DNA sequence:

    Template strand   3′— TAC TTT AAA GCG ATT —5′

    Nontemplate strand   5′— ATG AAA TTT CGC TAA —3′
- Use playdough or cut out pieces of paper to represent the various enzymes, ribosome subunits, amino acids, and other components.
- Use the pieces you assembled to build a dynamic (claymation-type) model of the processes of transcription and translation.
- When you feel you have developed a good working model, use it to explain the processes of transcription and translation to another student or to your instructor.

Use your model of transcription and translation to answer these questions.

1. How would you need to modify your model to include intron removal? Your explanation should contain definitions or descriptions of the following terms and structures:

    pre-mRNA   exons

    RNA splicing   spliceosome

    introns

2. If 20% of the DNA in a guinea pig cell is adenine, what percentage is cytosine? Explain your answer.

3. Several different types of RNA exist in prokaryotic and eukaryotic cells. List the three main types of RNA involved in transcription and translation. Answer the questions to complete the chart.

a. Types of RNA:	b. Where are they produced?	c. Where and how do they function in cells?

4. Given your understanding of transcription and translation, fill in the blanks below and indicate the 5′ and 3′ ends of each nucleotide sequence. Again, assume no RNA processing occurs.

Nontemplate strand of DNA: 5′ A T G T A T G C C A A T G C A 3′

Template strand of DNA: _′ T _ _ _ _ _ _ _ _ _ _ _ _ _ _′

mRNA: _′ A _ _ _ _ U _ _ _ _ _ _ _ _ _′

Anticodons on
    complementary tRNA: _′ _ _ _ / _ _ _ / _ _ _ / _ _ _ / _ _ _ / _ _′

5. Scientists struggled to understand how four bases could code for 20 different amino acids. If one base coded for one amino acid, the cell could produce only four different kinds of amino acids (4^1). If two bases coded for each amino acid, there would be four possible choices (of nucleotides) for the first base and four possible choices for the second base. This would produce 4^2 or 16 possible amino acids.

a. What is the maximum number of *three-letter codons* that can be produced using only four different nucleotide bases in DNA?

b. How many different codons could be produced if the codons were four bases long?

Mathematical logic indicates that at least three bases must code for each amino acid. This led scientists to ask:

- How can we determine whether this is true?
- Which combinations of bases code for each of the amino acids?

To answer these questions, scientists manufactured different artificial mRNA strands. When placed in appropriate conditions, the strands could be used to produce polypeptides.

Assume a scientist makes three artificial mRNA strands:

(*x*) 5′–AAAAAAAAAAAAAAAAAAAAAAAAAAAA–3′

(*y*) 5′–AAACCCAAACCCAAACCCAAACCCAAA–3′

(*z*) 5′–AUAUAUAUAUAUAUAUAUAUAUAUAU–3′

When he analyzes the polypeptides produced, he finds that:

x produces a polypeptide composed entirely of lysine.

y produces a polypeptide that is 50% lysine and 50% proline.

z produces a polypeptide that is 50% isoleucine and 50% tyrosine.

c. Do these results support the three-bases-per-codon or the four-bases-per-codon hypothesis? Explain.

d. This type of experiment was used to discover the mRNA nucleotide codons for each of the 20 amino acids. If you were doing these experiments, what sequences would you try next? Explain your logic.

6. Now that the complete genetic code has been determined, you can use the strand of DNA shown here and the codon chart in Figure 15.6 (page 284) in your textbook to answer the next questions.

Original template strand of DNA: 3′–TAC GCA AGC AAT ACC GAC GAA–5′

a. If this DNA strand produces an mRNA, what is the sequence of the mRNA?

b. For what sequence of amino acids does this mRNA code? (Assume it does not contain introns.)

c. The chart lists five point mutations that may occur in the original strand of DNA. What happens to the amino acid sequence or protein produced as a result of each mutation? (*Note:* Position 1 refers to the first base at the 3′ end of the transcribed strand. The last base in the DNA strand, at the 5′ end, is at position 21.)

Original template strand: 3′–TAC GCA AGC AAT ACC GAC GAA–5′

Mutation	Effect on amino acid sequence
i. Substitution of T for G at position 8	
ii. Addition of T between positions 8 and 9	
iii. Deletion of C at position 15	
iv. Substitution of T for C at position 18	
v. Deletion of C at position 18	
vi. Which of the mutations produces the greatest change in the amino acid sequence of the polypeptide coded for by this 21-base-pair gene?	

7. Sickle-cell disease is caused by a single base substitution in the gene for the beta subunit of hemoglobin. This base substitution changes one of the amino acids in the hemoglobin molecule from glutamate to valine. Look up the structures of glutamate (glu) and valine (val) on Figure 3.3, page 41 of your textbook. What kinds of changes in protein structure might result from this substitution? Explain.

8. Why do dentists and physicians cover patients with lead aprons when they take mouth or other X-rays?

9 to 13. During DNA replication, which of the following observations would you expect to be true? Explain your answers.

T/F   9.   More ligase would be associated with the lagging strand than with the leading strand.

T/F 10.   More primase would be used for the lagging strand than for the leading strand.

T/F 11.   More helicase would be associated with the lagging strand than with the leading strand.

T/F 12.   DNA ligase links the 3′ end of one Okazaki fragment to the 5′ end of the other Okazaki fragment in the lagging strand.

T/F 13.   In the lagging strand, the enzyme DNA polymerase III that produces the next Okazaki fragment also removes the short segment of primer RNA on the previous Okazaki fragment.

14.   You obtain a sample of double-stranded DNA and transcribe mRNA from this DNA. You then analyze the base composition of each of the two DNA strands and the one mRNA strand, and get the following results. The numbers indicate percentage of each base in the strand:

	A —	G —	C —	T —	U
strand 1	40.1 –	28.9 –	9.9 –	0.0 –	21.1
strand 2	21.5 –	9.5 –	29.9 –	39.1 –	0.0
strand 3	40.0 –	29.0 –	9.7 –	21.3 –	0.0

a. Which of these strands must be the mRNA? Explain.

b. Which one is the template strand for the mRNA? Explain.

15. In a new experiment, you obtain a different sample of double-stranded DNA and transcribe mRNA from this DNA. You then analyze the base composition of each of the two DNA strands and the one mRNA strand, and get the following results. The numbers indicate percentage of each base in the strand:

	A —	G —	C —	T —	U
strand 1	29.1 –	39.9 –	31.0 –	0.0 –	0.0
strand 2	0.0 –	30.9 –	39.8 –	30.2 –	0.0
strand 3	29.4 –	39.4 –	31.2 –	0.0 –	0.0

a. Which of these strands could be the mRNA? Explain.

b. Which one must be the template strand for the mRNA? Explain.

Name _____   Course/Section _____

Date _____   Professor/TA _____

Activity 17.1 How is gene expression controlled in bacteria?

Fill in the chart to organize what we know about the *lac* and *trp* operons.

Operon:	*lac*		*trp*	
Is the metabolic pathway anabolic or catabolic?				
What regulatory genes are associated with the operon, and what functions does each serve?	Genes:	Functions:	Genes:	Functions:

(Continued)

Operon:	*lac*		*trp*	
What structural genes are included in each operon and what does each produce?	Genes:	Products:	Genes:	Products:
Is the operon inducible or repressible?				
Is the repressor protein produced in active or inactive form?				
The repressor protein becomes active when it interacts with:				

Name _____ Course/Section _____

Date _____ Professor/TA _____

Activity 17.2 Modeling the *lac* and *trp* Operon Systems: How can gene expression be controlled in prokaryotes?

Using the information in Activity 17.1 and in Chapter 17 of *Biological Science*, 4th edition, construct a model or diagram of the normal operation of both the *lac* and *trp* operon systems.

In your models or diagrams, be sure to include these considerations:
>   regulatory and structural genes
>   inducible versus repressible control
>   anabolic versus catabolic enzyme activity
>   negative versus positive controls

Use your model to answer these questions.

1. Under what circumstances would the *lac* operon be "on" versus "off"?
    The *trp* operon?

2. How are the *lac* and *trp* operons similar (in structure, function, or both)?

3. What are the key differences between the *lac* and *trp* operons?

4. What advantages are gained by having genes organized into operons?

5. Strain X of *E. coli* contains a mutated *lac* regulatory gene on its bacterial genome. As a result, the gene produces a nonfunctional *lac* repressor protein. You add a plasmid (an extra circular piece of double-stranded DNA) to these cells. The plasmid contains a normal regulatory gene and a normal *lac* operon.

   Build a model or diagram of what one of these modified *E. coli* cells would look like. Then answer the questions and use your model or diagram to explain your answers.

   a. Before the addition of the plasmid, would the *E. coli* strain X cells be able to produce the enzymes for lactose digestion? Explain.

   b. After the addition of the plasmid, would the plasmidís *lac* operon produce the enzymes for lactose digestion constitutively (all the time) or only when lactose was the available sugar source? Explain.

   c. After the addition of the plasmid, would the bacterial genome's *lac* operon produce the enzymes for lactose digestion constitutively or only when lactose was the available energy source? Explain.

   d. If equal amounts of lactose and glucose were present in the cell, would the *lac* operon in the bacterial DNA be off or on? Would the *lac* operon on the introduced plasmid be off or on? Explain.

Name _____   Course/Section _____

Date _____   Professor/TA _____

  Activity 18.1 How is gene activity controlled in eukaryotes?

Human genes cannot all be active at the same time. If they were, all the cells in our bodies would look the same and have the same function(s). For specialization to occur, some genes or gene products must be active while others are turned off or inactive.

1. In eukaryotes, gene expression or gene product expression can be controlled at several different levels. Indicate what types of control might occur at each level of gene or gene product expression.

Level	Types of control
a. The gene or DNA itself	
b. The mRNA product of the gene	
c. The protein product of the mRNA	

2. Single-celled organisms like *Amoeba* and *Paramecia* often live in environments that change quickly. Which of the following types of control allow organisms like *Amoeba* to respond most quickly to frequent short-term environmental changes? Explain your reasoning.

a. Control of mRNA transcription from DNA

b. Control of enzyme concentration by controlling the rate of mRNA translation

c. Control of activity of existing enzymes

d. Control of the amount of DNA present in the cell

Name ——————————————— Course/Section ———————————————

Date ——————————————— Professor/TA ———————————————

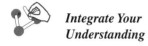 *Integrate Your*
Understanding **Chapters 19–20 (1)—How and why are genes cloned into recombinant DNA vectors?**

Develop a model to explain how a human gene can be cloned into a bacterial plasmid. Your model should be a dynamic (working or active) representation of the events that need to occur in order to

- clone the insulin gene into a bacterial plasmid and
- transform the plasmid into *E. coli.*

When you develop and explain your model, be sure to include definitions or descriptions of the following terms and components:

restriction enzyme(s)

ligase

plasmid DNA

human mRNA (the mRNA for insulin)

reverse transcriptase

transformation

E. coli marker genes (an antibiotic resistance gene)

cloning vector

Building the Model

- Use chalk on a tabletop, or a marker on a large sheet of paper, to draw at least two test tubes and an *E. coli* cell's plasma membrane. The *E. coli* should have a diameter of at least 12 inches. The test tubes should have a width of at least 6 inches. Use the test tubes for producing the insulin gene and for cloning the gene into the plasmid. Then transform your recombinant plasmid into the *E. coli* cell.
- Use playdough or cut out pieces of paper to represent the enzymes, RNA molecules, and other components.

- Use the pieces you assembled to develop a dynamic (claymation-type) model to demonstrate how a gene can be cloned into a plasmid and how the plasmid can then be transformed into a bacterial cell.
- When you feel you have developed a good working model, demonstrate it to another student or to your instructor.

Use your model to answer these questions.

1. Prior to recombinant gene technology, the insulin required to treat diabetes was obtained from the pancreases of slaughtered farm animals. Because the insulin was from other species, some humans developed immune responses or allergic reactions to it. As recombinant gene technology advanced, researchers explored the possibility of incorporating the human insulin gene into a plasmid that could be transformed into *E. coli*. If this technology was successful, the *E. coli* would produce human insulin that could be harvested from the bacterial culture medium.

   Researchers first needed to isolate the gene for insulin. To do this, they isolated mRNA (rather than DNA) from the beta cells of human pancreas tissue. Using reverse transcriptase, they made double-stranded DNA molecules that were complementary to the mRNA molecules they extracted from the pancreas cells.

   a. Based on what you know about eukaryotic chromosomes and genes, why did researchers choose to isolate mRNA rather than DNA?

   b. What further adjustments might researchers need to make in the DNA molecules produced by reverse transcriptase before the molecules could be incorporated into bacterial plasmids?

   c. Not all the DNA molecules produced by reverse transcription from pancreatic mRNA contained the gene for insulin. Some contained other genes. What mechanisms can be used to locate those bacterial colonies that picked up plasmids containing any of the genes produced by reverse transcription from pancreatic mRNAs?

d. What mechanisms can be used to locate bacterial colonies that picked up only plasmids containing the insulin gene? (*Note:* Today almost all the insulin used for the treatment of human diabetes is produced using recombinant technology.)

Name —————————————   Course/Section —————————————

Date —————————————   Professor/TA —————————————

Integrate Your
Understanding **Chapters 19–20 (2)—How can PCR be used to
amplify specific genes?**

1. Assume you are using PCR to make multiple copies of a gene (shaded in gray below).

    DNA containing gene of interest:
    3′–TATAAAGACTTACAAATTTGTCCCCATTTTGC–5′
    5′–ATATTTCTGAATGTTTAAACAGGGGTAAAACG–3′

On separate sheets of paper, describe the overall process and diagram the results you would obtain for 1, 2, and 3 rounds of PCR replication using the primers, ATGTT and CCATT.

(*Note:* For simplicity we are showing DNA primers that are only 5 bases in length. In actual use, the DNA primers used are at least 17 bases long. This length is used to help reduce the risk that the primer anneals with—base-pairs with—anything other than the specific segment of DNA to be amplified.)

2. PCR (polymerase chain reaction) is often used in forensics to amplify small amounts of DNA found at crime scenes. The amplified DNA is then tested for differences in RFLP (restriction fragment length polymorphisms) or STR (single tandem repeat) lengths.

    a. Explain what RFLPs and STRs are.

    b. How do STRs compare for unrelated individuals versus for closely related individuals (for example, parent and child or brother and sister)?

    c. How reliable are these types of DNA fingerprinting for identifying individuals? What factors affect their reliability?

3. The use of DNA technology in forensics.

   a. After undergoing electrophoresis, the gel in the figure below shows the RFLP analysis of DNA samples obtained from a crime scene. Blood stains on a suspect's shirt (B) were analyzed and compared with blood from the victim (V) and from the suspect (S). Are the blood stains on the shirt from the victim or from the suspect? Explain.

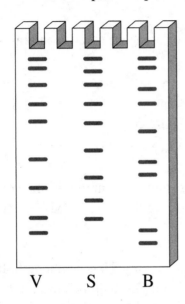

b. Investigators find an additional blood sample in the garage, but they are not sure whether it is related to the crime. After undergoing electrophoresis, the gel in the figure below shows the results of DNA fingerprinting of blood samples obtained from the victim (V), her husband (H), the suspect (S), and the blood from the garage (B$_2$). Is the blood from the garage related to the crime? Explain your answer.

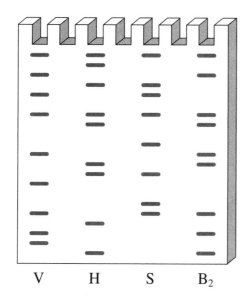

4. Which of the following sequences (on one strand of a double-stranded DNA molecule) is likely to be a cleavage site for a restriction enzyme? Explain your answer.

    a. CGTACC

    b. ATGTCG

    c. GATATG

    d. TGCGCA

    e. TGGCCG

Name ——————————————   Course/Section ————————————————

Date ——————————————   Professor/TA ————————————————

Integrate Your
Understanding **Chapters 19–20 (3)—How can we discover the**
sequence of an organism's DNA?

Bacterial genomes have between 1 and 6 million base pairs (Mb). Most plants and animals have about 100 Mb. Humans have approximately 2900 Mb. As a result, individual chromosomes may contain millions of base pairs. It is difficult to work with DNA sequences this large. As a result, the DNA is broken into smaller pieces (approximately 500 to 1000 bp each). These pieces are sequenced and then the sequenced pieces are examined and aligned based on overlapping sequence homology at their ends.

By comparing the DNA sequences among organisms, scientists can determine:

- what parts of the genomes are most similar among organisms and therefore likely evolved earliest,

- what key changes exist in the genomes that may account for differences among related species,

- what changes within species exist that may account for development of specific types of disease.

The following activity has been designed to help you understand how genomes are sequenced and how the sequence information may be used.

1. In 1980, Frederick Sanger was awarded the Nobel Prize for inventing the dideoxy method (or Sanger method) of DNA sequencing. A double-stranded DNA segment approximately 700 bp in length is heated (or treated chemically) to separate the two strands. The single-stranded DNA that results is placed into a test tube containing a 9-to-1 ratio of normal deoxynucleotides to dideoxynucleotides. A dideoxynucleotide has no –OH group at either the 2′ or 3′ carbon. As a result, whenever a dideoxynucleotide is added to the growing DNA strand, synthesis stops at that point. If the ratio of normal to dideoxynucleotides is high enough, where one will be included in the sequence is random.

Using this method, you set up each of 4 test tubes as noted below:

Tube number	Deoxynucleotide	Dideoxynucleotide
1	dATP, dTTP, dGTP, dCTP	ddATP
2	dATP, dTTP, dGTP, dCTP	ddTTP
3	dATP, dTTP, dGTP, dCTP	ddGTP
4	dATP, dTTP, dGTP, dCTP	ddCTP

All tubes contain the same single-stranded DNA molecules and the same primers. All other enzymes and materials that are required for DNA replication are present in each tube. You allow the replication to continue for the same length of time in each tube. At the end of the time period, you extract the DNA from each tube and run it on an agarose gel. You dye the gel with ethidium bromide and observe the following banding patterns on the gel.

(*Note:* For this demonstration, we are using a DNA strand that is only 20 bp in length.)

a. Which band in the gel contains the shortest DNA strand? What is the identity of its terminal ddNTP?

Integrate Your Understanding Chapters 19–20 (3)

b. Which band contains the next shortest DNA strand? What is the identity of its terminal ddNTP?

c. Continue reading the terminal ddNTP of each band from shortest to longest to determine the linear sequence of nucleotides in the DNA strand complement. What is the sequence?

2. The Sanger method has since been modified so that each ddNTP used is now flagged with an identifying fluorescent tag such that ddTTP fluoresces red; ddGTP, yellow; ddCTP, blue; and ddATP, green.

a. Assume that you run the same experiment that you did above. However, this time you combine all of the different nucleotides (both dNTPs and ddNTPs) in the same test tube. Your run the products of the reaction on the following gel. Draw the bands you would see on the gel using the appropriate fluorescent colors (ddTTP fluoresces red; ddGTP, yellow; ddCTP, blue; and ddATP, green).

Band sequence for combined experiment

b. Draw the image you would see from an optical scan of the gel above, as is shown in Figure 19.9 on page 347 of *Biological Science*, 4th edition.

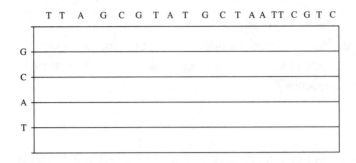

c. Assume that this is a gene from a normal individual. Compare the optical image you generated in part b to the optical image from an individual with a hypothetical genetic disease. This disease results from nonproduction of a necessary gene product. What and where is the mutation in the gene sequence? Why might this particular mutation lead to nonproduction of a protein?

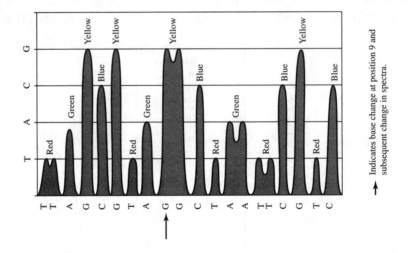

3. To help determine evolutionary relationships among different groups of organisms, scientists compare gene sequences of highly conserved genes. What are "highly conserved genes"? Give examples and indicate what is "highly conserved" and why.

4. What types of DNA do scientists use to determine individual identities of organisms within the same species? Why do they use this type of DNA?

Name_____   Course/Section_____

Date_____   Professor/TA_____

 Activity 21.1 How can the development of an organism be controlled at the cellular and molecular levels?

The critical events that occur in the development of all multicellular organisms include zygote formation, cell division, induction, determination and differentiation, and morphogenesis.

1. Describe the function(s) of each of the following events in development.

Stage of development	General function
a. Zygote formation	
b. Cell division	
c. Differential gene expression	
d. Determination and differentiation	
e. Morphogenesis	

2. *Drosophila melanogaster*, the fruit fly, has been used as a model organism to study development. As a result of these studies (and others), we now realize that normal development involves hierarchies of spatially and temporally regulated gene expression.

    a. What general approach(es) did researchers take to find the genes responsible for normal development in *Drosophila*? For example, what types of observations did they make, and what method(s) did they use?

3. Using these methods, researchers have discovered that development occurs due to the sequential expression of a variety of genes. Many of these are genes for transcription factors. As Nüsslein-Volhard and Wieschaus discovered, in *Drosophila*, the basic sequence or flow of development can be outlined as shown below.

        Maternal effects genes (for example, *bicoid*)
              \
          Gap genes
               \
            Pair-rule genes
                  \
              Segment polarity genes
                     \
                  Homeotic genes (or homeobox, *Hox*, genes)
                     \
                    Master regulatory genes (for example, *myoD*)

    a. What does each type of gene control in the development of the fruit fly?

b. Based on your answers in part (a), if you wanted to produce a mutation that caused profound effects (drastic effects) on the overall development of the organism, where in the sequence would you introduce the mutation? Explain your answer.

c. What phenotype change(s) might you see if a developing fruit fly had a mutation in a gap gene? In a segment polarity gene?

4. What, if any, similarities and differences are found when *Drosophila* development is compared with development in other organisms like a frog, a mouse, or a human? What do the findings indicate about the evolution of these organisms?

Name_____   Course/Section_____

Date_____   Professor/TA_____

Extend Your
Understanding **Activity 21.2 An experiment designed to test the
genetics of development**

To look for new genes affecting development, a researcher treats male fruit flies with a mutagen. In the P generation, each of the males is then mated individually with a normal untreated female. F_1 offspring from each cross are mated with each other, again with only one male and one female per mating vial. F_2 offspring from each of these crosses are again mated with each other as above. The resulting F_3 offspring are again crossed as above.

What results would you expect from these matings if a mutant development phenotype were the result of:

    a. a dominant mutant allele

    b. a recessive mutant allele

    c. mutant maternal genetic input to the egg

Name_____   Course/Section_____

Date_____   Professor/TA_____

Activity 22.1 What major events occur in animal development?

1. In biology, males and females are defined based on the types of gametes they
    produce. Males produce smaller, motile gametes; and females produce larger,
    nonmotile gametes.

    In your text, sperm are described as "DNA with propellers" or "race cars." In
    contrast, eggs are described as "semitrailers." What aspects of the structure and
    function of (a) sperm and (b) eggs make these good analogies?

    a. Sperm:

    b. Eggs:

2. The early stages in the development of all vertebrates (and many other animal
    species) include zygote formation, cleavage, blastula formation, gastrula formation,
    and organogenesis.

    Among the major aspects of development are cell adhesion/recognition, cell growth
    (in size and/or number), cell determination, and cell differentiation.

    Fill in the chart on the next page to indicate:

    a. What key events occur at each of the stages of development?

    b. Which of the major aspects of development are involved in each stage of
        development?

Stages of Development	Zygote formation	Cleavage and Blastula formation	Gastrula formation	Organogenesis
a. Summary of key events for each stage				
b. Aspects of development that occur during this stage:				
Cell adhesion/ recognition				
Cell growth (size or number?)				
Determination				
Differentiation				

Name_____   Course/Section_____

Date_____   Professor/TA_____

Extend Your
Understanding   **Activity 22.2 Animal Development: Sample Exam Questions**

Questions 1 and 2. For each situation described, choose the graph that fits best.

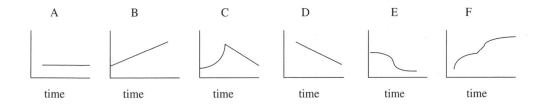

1. Which graph best describes the change in size of individual cells of a vertebrate
    embryo from the time of zygote formation to the end of cleavage? Explain your
    answer.

2. Which graph best describes the change in the number of cells in the embryo from
    fertilization to gastrulation? Explain your answer.

Questions 3 to 6. While the mechanics of gastrulation may differ among various
organisms, the overall objectives and problems are the same. Which of the following are
accomplished by the end of gastrulation?

T/F   3.   formation of the three germ layers (i.e. ectoderm, mesoderm, and endoderm)

T/F   4.   establishment of the embryonic axis (anterior to posterior)

T/F   5.   determination of the fates of the individual cells of the gastrula

T/F   6.   formation of the neural tube

7. In a now classic experiment, Spemann and Mangold took cells from the dorsal lip of the blastopore from one frog embryo and transplanted them to an area opposite the dorsal lip in another frog embryo (the host). As a result, the host embryo developed two heads, one at the site of the "new" or transplanted dorsal lip and the other at the site of the host's original dorsal lip. A thorough examination indicated that *the second head was formed from host cells*. Which of the following developmental cues or mechanisms was most likely the trigger (or cause) for the generation of the second head? Explain your answer.

A. cytoplasmic determinants, which are unequally distributed in the host embryo
B. gradients set up in the egg, which gave rise to the host embryo
C. *Hox* genes (or *homeobox* genes) present in the embryo receiving the transplant
D. cell–cell signaling between the transplanted dorsal lip and the host embryo
E. all of the above

Name_____   Course/Section_____

Date_____   Professor/TA_____

 Activity 23.1 What major events occur in plant development?

1. What key differences exist in form and function of plants versus animals?

2. The fundamental differences that exist in plant cell structure also dictate that plant development must differ from animal development. Which aspects of plant development differ significantly from animal development and which are similar?

Note: To give yourself enough space for the answers, recreate the table below on your computer or on a larger sheet of paper.

Aspect of plant development	Differences from animal development	Similarities to animal development
Gamete formation		
Zygote formation		
Embryogenesis		
Vegetative development		
Reproductive development		

Activity 23.2 The Developmental Genetics of Floral Structure Mutations

Questions 1 and 2. In studying the development of flowers, Meyerowitz and colleagues found three general classes of floral mutants:

- Mutants with only carpels and stamens
- Mutants with only sepals and carpels
- Mutants with only petals and sepals

From this they developed their ABC model of how three genes interacted under normal conditions to form the four whorls of the flower: sepals, petals, stamens, and carpel.

In their model, each of the three organ identity genes is expressed in two adjacent whorls such that if the *A* gene's protein is produced alone, sepals are formed. If the proteins from both the *A* and *B* genes are produced, petals are formed. If the proteins from genes *B* and *C* are both produced, stamens are formed. If only the protein from gene *C* is produced, carpels are formed (Figure 23.13) Page 411, *Biological Science,* 4th edition.

Given the mutants (listed above) that they found, they also proposed that the presence of A protein inhibits C protein production and the presence of C protein similarly inhibits the production of A protein.

1. What floral phenotype would have resulted if the *A* gene was lacking and no inhibition between A and C protein production existe?

2. What floral phenotype would have resulted if the *C* gene was lacking and no inhibition between A and C production existed?

3. What floral phenotype would have resulted if the *B* gene was lacking and no inhibition between A and C production existed?

4. Compare your answers to 1–3 above to the drawings of the actual mutants in Figure 23.12, Page 410, *Biological Science,* 4th edition.

   a. How do they differ?

   b. Does proposing the mutual inhibition of *A* and *C* gene production explain these actual mutants?

Name_____   Course/Section_____

Date_____   Professor/TA_____

Activity 24.1 How did Darwin view evolution via natural selection?

Darwin is remembered not because he was the first to propose that evolution occurs. Many others had presented this idea before. Instead, he is remembered for defining the mechanism behind evolution—that is, the theory of natural selection. To do this, Darwin integrated, or put together, information from a wide range of sources. Some of this information was provided by others; some he observed on his own.

Working alone or in groups of three or four, construct a concept map of Darwin's view of evolution via natural selection. Be sure to include definitions or descriptions of all the terms in the list below. Keep in mind that there are many ways to construct a concept map.

- Begin by writing each term on a separate Post-it note or piece of paper.
- Then organize the terms into a map that indicates how the terms are associated or related.
- Draw lines between terms, and add action phrases to the lines that indicate how the terms are related.
- When you finish your map, explain it to another group of students.

Here is an example:

$$\boxed{Embryology} \xrightarrow{\text{provides evidence for}} \boxed{Evolution}$$

TERMS

fact	Darwin	fit individuals
biogeography	vertebrate limb structure	fossil record
gradualism	species population	embryology
uniformitarianism	individual	taxonomy
theory	variability	selective (domestic)
Galápagos Islands	paleontology	breeding
evolution	Malthus	limited resources
homology	population size	struggle for existence
natural selection	environment or	reproduction
analogy	resources	extinction

Name_____   Course/Section_____

Use the understanding you gained from creating the concept map to answer these questions.

1. In the 1860s, what types of evidence were available to indicate that evolution had occurred on Earth?

2. How did knowledge of mechanisms of artificial selection (used in developing various strains of domesticated animals and plants) help Darwin understand how evolution could occur?

Activity 24.1

3. Based on his studies, Darwin made some observations; they are listed in the chart. Complete the chart by answering how Darwin made the observations.

Observation	What did Darwin read or observe that led him to this observation?
a. All species populations have the reproduction potential to increase exponentially over time.	
b. The number of individuals in natural populations tends to remain stable over time.	
c. Environmental resources are limited.	
d. Individuals in a population vary in their characteristics.	
e. Much of this variation is heritable.	

4. Based on these observations, Darwin made some inferences. Which of the observation(s) in question 3 allowed Darwin to make each inference?

Inference	Observations that led to the inference
a. Production of more individuals than the environment can support leads to a struggle for existence such that only a fraction of the offspring survive each generation.	
b. Survival for existence is not random. Those individuals whose inherited traits best fit them to the environment are likely to leave more offspring than less fit individuals do.	
c. The unequal ability of individuals to survive and reproduce leads to a gradual change in the population, with favorable characteristics accumulating over the generations.	

5. Based on these observations and inferences, how did Darwin define fitness?

6. How did Darwin define evolution?

7. What is the unit of natural selection? (What is selected?) What is the unit of evolution? (What evolves?)

8. In a population of mice, some individuals have brown fur and some have black fur. At present, both phenotypes are equally fit. What could happen to change the relative fitness of the two phenotypes in the population? For example, what could cause individuals with brown fur to show reduced fitness relative to individuals with black fur?

9. Assume you discover a new world on another planet that is full of organisms.

    a. What characteristics would you look for to determine that these organisms arose as a result of evolutionary processes?

    b. What characteristics would you look for to determine that these organisms did *not* arise as the result of evolutionary processes?

10. Why is it incorrect to say that vertebrates evolved eyes in order to see?

Name_____   Course/Section_____

Date_____   Professor/TA_____

 Activity 24.2 How do Darwin's and Lamarck's ideas about evolution differ?

Early in the 1800s Lamarck proposed a theory of evolution. He suggested that traits acquired during an organism's life—for example, larger muscles—could be passed on to its offspring. The idea of inheritance of acquired characteristics was popular for many years. No such mechanism is implied in Darwin's theory of evolution via natural selection, however. After Darwin published his work, scientists conducted many experiments to disprove the inheritance of acquired traits. By the middle of the 20th century, enough data had accumulated to make even its most adamant supporters give up the idea of inheritance of acquired characteristics.

Given your understanding of both Lamarck's and Darwin's ideas about evolution, determine whether the statements on the next page are more Lamarckian or more Darwinian. If the statement is Lamarckian, change it to make it Darwinian. Here are two example statements and answers.

Examples

A. The widespread use of DDT in the mid-1900s put pressure on insect populations to evolve resistance to DDT. As a result, large populations of insects today are resistant to DDT.

Answer: This is a Lamarckian statement. DDT worked only against insects that had no DDT-resistance genes. The genes for DDT resistance had to be present for insects to survive DDT use in the first place.

Suggested change: Wide-scale use of DDT in the mid-1900s selected against insects that had no resistance to DDT. Only the insects that were resistant to DDT survived. These insects mated and passed their resistance genes on to their offspring. As a result, large populations of insects today are resistant to DDT.

B. According to one theory, the dinosaurs became extinct because they couldn't evolve fast enough to deal with climatic changes that affected their food and water supplies.

Answer: This is a quasi-Lamarckian statement. Organisms do not purposefully evolve. (Genetic recombination experiments are perhaps an exception.) Once you are conceived, your genes are not going to change; that is, you are not going to evolve. The genetic composition of a species population can change over time as certain genotypes are selected against. Genes determine phenotypes. The environmental conditions may favor the phenotype produced by one genotype more than that produced by another.

Suggested change: According to one theory, the dinosaurs became extinct because their physiological and behavioral characteristics were too specialized to allow them to survive the rapid changes in climate that occurred. The climatic changes caused changes in the dinosaurs' food and water supplies. Because none of the dinosaurs survived, the genes and associated phenotypes that would have led to their survival must not have been present in the populations.

Statements

1. Many of the bacterial strains that infect humans today are resistant to a wide range of antibiotics. These resistant strains were not so numerous or common prior to the use of antibiotics. These strains must have appeared or evolved in response to the use of the antibiotics.
2. Life arose in the aquatic environment and later invaded land. Once animals came onto land, they had to evolve effective methods of support against gravity and locomotion in order to survive.

3. A given phenotypic trait—for example, height, speed, tooth structure—(and therefore the genes that determine it) may have positive survival or selective value, negative survival or selective value, or neutral (neither positive nor negative) survival or selective value. Which of these it has depends on the environmental conditions the organism encounters.

4. The children of bodybuilders tend to be much more athletic, on average, than other children because the characteristics and abilities gained by their parents have been passed on to the children.

Name_____   Course/Section_____

Date_____   Professor/TA_____

 Activity 24.3 How would you evaluate these explanations of Darwin's ideas?

Unfortunately, even today some people get or give the impression that acquired characteristics can be inherited. As a result, we need to be very careful about how we state our understanding of evolution and evolutionary theory.

To test understanding of Darwin's ideas, this question was included on an exam.

> *4-point question:*
> *In two or three sentences, describe Darwin's theory of descent with modification and the mechanism, natural selection, that he proposed to explain how this comes about.*

Four student answers to the question are given. Based on what you know about Darwinian evolution and natural selection, evaluate and grade how well each answer represents Darwin's ideas. For any answer that does not receive full credit (4 points), be sure to indicate why points were lost.

Student 1. Darwin saw that populations increased faster than the ability of the land to support them could increase, so that individuals must struggle for limited resources. He proposed that individuals with some inborn advantage over others would have a better chance of surviving and reproducing offspring and so be naturally selected. As time passes, these advantageous characteristics accumulate and change the species into a new species.

Student 2. Darwin's theory of evolution explains how new species arise from already existing ones. In his mechanism of natural selection, organisms with favorable traits tend to survive and reproduce more successfully, while those that lack the traits do not. Beneficial traits are passed on to future generations in this manner, and a new species will be created in the end!

Student 3. Descent with modification using natural selection was Darwin's attempt at explaining evolution. An organism is modified by its surroundings, activities, and lifestyle. These modifications, by natural selection, make the organism better suited to its life.

Student 4. Darwin's theory states that organisms can become modified by environmental conditions or use or disuse features and that the modifications can be passed down to succeeding generations. He proposes that nature selects for a characteristic trait that is beneficial to the survival of the organisms and that organisms would pass on this trait.